Mathematics 9

Exploring the Concepts

Teacher's Resource

Rod Yeager

Orangeville, Ontario

T. Anne Yeager

Orangeville, Ontario

 **McGraw-Hill Ryerson**

Toronto   Montréal   Boston   Burr Ridge, IL   Dubuque, IA   Madison, WI   New York
San Francisco   St. Louis   Bangkok   Bogotá   Caracas   Kuala Lumpur   Lisbon   London   Madrid
Mexico City   Milan   New Delhi   Santiago   Seoul   Singapore   Sydney   Taipei

McGraw-Hill
Ryerson Limited

A Subsidiary of The McGraw-Hill Companies

Mathematics 9: Exploring the Concepts
Teacher's Resource

ISBN 0-07-089892-8

http://www.mcgrawhill.ca

1 2 3 4 5 6 7 8 9 0   CP   0 9 8 7 6 5 4 3 2

Printed and bound in Canada

The Geometer's Sketchpad® is a registered trademark of Key Curriculum Press, 1150 65th Street, Emeryville, CA 94608, 1-800-995-MATH.
CBL™ and CBR™ are trademarks of Texas Instruments Incorporated.
Graphmatica is shareware distributed by kSoft, Inc. For more information or to download the current version, please visit *http://www.graphmatica.com/*

National Library of Canada Cataloguing in Publication Data

Yeager, Rod
   Mathematics 9 : exploring the concepts. Teacher's resource

ISBN 0-07-089892-8

1. Mathematics—Study and teaching (Secondary)
2. Mathematics—Problems, exercises, etc. I. Yeager, T. Anne
II. Yeager, T. Anne. Mathematics 9. III. Title.
IV. Title: Mathematics nine

QA39.2.Y43 2002 Suppl.1   510   C2002-900306-7

PUBLISHER: Diane Wyman
DEVELOPMENTAL EDITOR: Sheila Bassett
SENIOR SUPERVISING EDITOR: Carol Altilia
PERMISSIONS EDITOR: Maria DeCambra
EDITORIAL ASSISTANT: Erin Parton
ASSISTANT PROJECT COORDINATORS: Melissa Nippard, Janie Reeson
PRODUCTION SUPERVISOR: Yolanda Pigden
PRODUCTION COORDINATOR: Jennifer Wilkie
INTERIOR DESIGN: Jay Tee Graphics Ltd.
ELECTRONIC PAGE MAKE-UP: Jay Tee Graphics Ltd.
COVER DESIGN: Dianna Little
COVER IMAGE: © COMSTOCK/Henri Georgi

CONTENTS

Overview and Use of *Mathematics 9: Exploring the Concepts, Teacher's Resource* for Grade 9 Applied

1. The introduction includes the basic philosophy of the student resource. The characteristics and needs of the students in the applied mathematics course, and general teaching strategies that are effective for these students, are discussed.

2. Use the lesson planner side by side with the student resource. At times, the planner refers to several student resource activities together in a logical order. This is intended to simplify the process and group ideas/concepts together, so teacher planning can be done in two-to-five-day periods. All indicated times are approximate and may vary according to the needs and background of the students in the class.

3. Words in the student resource that are in **bold print** require a definition. Be prepared for this.

4. **Specific Expectations** The codes for the specific expectations are given in the margin beside each activity in the Teaching Notes. The specific expectation corresponding to each specific expectation code is given in full in the Correlation that begins on page viii.

5. **Related Resources** These also are provided in the left column of the Teaching Notes and, unless otherwise indicated, are taken from *MATHPOWER™ 9, Ontario Edition, Blackline Masters,* McGraw Hill Ryerson 1999.

6. **Common Errors** These comments indicate areas in which some students may have difficulties.

7. **Assessment Masters** Each unit in this teacher's resource has several short assessment activities (some could be formative) and a full summative assessment for the end of the unit. These can be marked in the traditional manner, using rubrics, checklists, or a combination of these. The generic rubrics provided by the Ministry of Education and Training and OAME are useful tools. The achievement chart categories (thinking inquiry/problem solving, application, knowledge and understanding, and communication) are not indicated, because different individuals and schools have their own criteria for what constitutes each of these categories, and weight them differently. Teachers can add this to each assessment as they see fit.

8. **Final Assessment and Exam** The teachers can provide a final summative assessment in the form of a set of activities/problems with a common theme. The intention would be to integrate and highlight many of the expectations in the course. Some schools may also choose to have a final exam. These are not provided.

9. The **Completion Awards** for each section, found at the end of each unit of the student resource, can be used in several ways, including any or all of the following:
   a) as a symbol of closure and satisfaction for the student
   b) as a teacher check for completion (The teacher can initial under the signature.)
   c) as a parent communication (The parent can initial under the signature.)
   d) as a pair–share, where partners can initial each other's book
   e) as a form of record keeping and accountability (The teacher can collect these and keep them on record.)
   f) as a form of formative assessment in each of the achievement chart categories (The teacher can choose one or two relevant questions from that section to mark by levels.)

   The students will know when to refer to the Completion Awards page when they come to the ✔ symbol.

Mathematics 9: Exploring the Concepts, Grade 9 Applied Philosophy, Overview, and Strategies

The expectations for grade 9 applied and academic mathematics courses are very similar, but the students are quite different. Generally, grade 9 applied mathematics students have difficulty with mathematics and some difficulty with language skills. With the emphasis on language and communication in the new math curriculum, this creates a further challenge for the students and the teacher.

The primary challenge in the applied class is that often these students are weak in reading, writing, and basic math skills. Their difficulty with multi-step problems can exasperate the situation. Students with learning disabilities and behavioural difficulties are often placed into the applied classes. Clearly, the grade 9 applied class is a challenge. The applied students can, however, be successful in achieving the required outcomes when careful planning and appropriate teaching strategies are employed.

Treating the students with understanding and respect is the first key to relating to, and, consequently, teaching these students. A multi-modal approach to teaching/learning is suggested. That is, students are most successful if they see, hear, and do everything. Activities, demonstrations, cooperative learning groups of two to four students for activities or discussion, student presentations, and some limited traditional "chalk and talk" teaching will accommodate different learning styles. A textbook format is not always compatible with the needs of these students. Difficulty tracking from text to paper, the reading level, open-ended questions, and the limited number of the "same" kind of question often create stumbling blocks to success and consolidation of concepts.

This student resource considers student reading level and varied learning needs, such as consistent formatting, chunking, and appropriate spacing for answers. Furthermore, the scaffolding is built in to assist the student in seeing the progression that is necessary in problem solving. Be sure you understand the goal of each section before doing it with the students. Similarly, try the experiments and technology activities so you can troubleshoot problems before the students walk into them. Being organized and familiar with the activity sheets before class often alleviates possible classroom management problems.

You might find it advantageous to make overheads of many of the student resource pages, particularly those that will be used to teach the concept. This will allow the students to follow along easily, and to take notes by filling in the blanks with teacher instruction. Taking up the activity pages from overheads is also very effective. Furthermore, overhead use allows you to make consistent eye contact, which increases attention and decreases behavioural problems. However, making use of all modes of delivery (overhead, chalkboard, white board, videos, flip charts, and so on) is most effective in keeping students interested and focused.

Communication with the home is essential, since you need parental support. When parents are aware of the expectations for their child, they are usually very supportive. Form letters that must be signed and returned, sent home five or six times throughout the semester, are very effective. These can have a place for comments to personalize as necessary. This is a worthwhile investment of time.

Technology is used as appropriate, with student-friendly language. Let the students use their personal calculators whenever the purpose of the lesson is anything other than number facts. Graphing calculators and the computer exercises provide a different medium for learning concepts. Some students are far more adept at technology than others, and this provides an opportunity to pair students who then can assist one another in learning.

The student resource covers all the expectations outlined in *The Ontario Curriculum, Foundations of Mathematics, Grade 9 Applied* document, 1999. However, depending on the strengths and the background of your class, it may be necessary to supplement the activities with additional material to solidify basic skills. Do review as required, within each unit. This makes the review relevant to the students, since they use it immediately. This holds true also for activities using technology. There are many resources containing supplementary material and review, and several probably exist on your shelf already.

Summative assessments provided in this teacher's resource include activities, quizzes, tests, and summative evaluations. The assessments provide opportunities for students to show knowledge/understanding, thinking skills, and problem solving. Communication can take many forms, such as, oral reports, written reports, demonstrations, and presentations. Often the students can show and tell better than they can write their understanding and solution. These opportunities must be provided to accommodate the different learning styles and the learning-disabled students. Be willing to read and write for those students with identified learning disabilities. Our goal is to teach the students the grade 9 math curriculum. An identified learning disability should not prevent the student from learning and being successful with the expectations of this mathematics course.

The following are some other strategies for helping the student learn. Vary teaching techniques within a single class. Build movement and discussion into each lesson. Provide structure without rigidity. Be ready to change gears when what you are doing is not working. Be sure the students see, hear, and understand the focus of each day's lesson. Remember, if students do not learn the way we teach, then it is our responsibility to teach the way they learn.

This student resource is about student success in the new curriculum. When students are having success, they tend to be cooperative and receptive, and they learn. But the student resource does not work independently of good teaching. Having the pre-made activities and assessments that are appropriate for the student, and that ensure coverage of the expectations, will allow the teacher time to concentrate on teaching strategies. Teachers can focus some energy on specific student needs, and on communication with the home. As class weaknesses are realized, the teacher can search out additional material as required. Furthermore, the student resource provides a logical and organized format to proceed through the course, and gives the student a long-term resource for future mathematics.

Grade 9 students in the applied course can be successful with this course when the material is presented to them at their level and in their learning style. We wish you success with your students.

Correlation of the Expectations of *The Ontario Curriculum, Foundations of Mathematics, Grade 9 Applied* With *Mathematics 9: Exploring the Concepts*

Strand: Number Sense and Algebra

Expectation Code	Specific Expectation	Student Resource Section/Activity	Student Resource Page Reference
NA1.01	determine strategies for mental mathematics and estimation, and apply these strategies throughout the course	Throughout	
NA1.02	demonstrate facility in operations with integers, as necessary to support other topics of the course (e.g., polynomials, equations, analytic geometry)	1.4A, 1.4B, 1.4C, 1.6A, 2.1D, 2.2A, 2.3A, 2.3B, 2.3C. 2.3D, 2.3E, 2.6, 3.1D	42–48, 58–59, 75–77, 79–88, 105, 133–135,
NA1.03	demonstrate facility in operations with percent, ratio and rate, and rational numbers, as necessary to support other topics of the course	1.1A, 1.1B, 1.1C, 1.6A, 2.4A, 2.4B, 2.4C, 2.4D	2–7, 58–59, 89–96
NA1.04	use a scientific calculator effectively for applications that arise throughout	1.6A, 2.2A, and throughout	58–59, 79–81, and throughout
NA1.05	judge the reasonableness of answers to problems by considering likely results within the situation described in the problem	1.6A, and throughout	58–59, and throughout
NA1.06	judge the reasonableness of answers produced by a calculator, a computer, or pencil and paper, using mental mathematics and estimation	1.6A, and throughout	58–59, and throughout
NA2.01	evaluate numerical expressions involving natural-number exponents with rational-number bases	2.1A, 2.1B, 3.3C	66–72, 148
NA2.02	substitute into and evaluate algebraic expressions involving exponents, to support other topics of the course (e.g., measurement, analytic geometry)	2.1C, 3.3B, 3.3C, 3.3D	73–74, 145–147
NA2.03	determine the meaning of negative exponents and of zero as an exponent from activities involving graphing, using technology, and from activities involving patterning	2.1D, 2.1E, 2.2A	75–78, 79–81, 148
NA2.04	represent very large and very small numbers using scientific notation	2.2A	79–81
NA2.05	enter and interpret exponential notation on a scientific calculator, as necessary, in calculations involving very large and very small numbers	2.1A, 2.2A	66–68, 79–81
NA2.06	determine, from the examination of patterns, the exponent rules for multiplying and dividing monomials and the exponent rule for the power of a power, and apply these rules in expressions involving one variable	2.1C	73–74
NA3.01	add and subtract polynomials, and multiply a polynomial by a monomial	2.3A, 2.3B, 2.3E	82–84, 88
NA3.02	expand and simplify polynomial expressions involving one variable	2.3A, 2.3B, 2.3E	82–84, 88
NA3.03	solve first-degree equations, excluding equations with fractional coefficients, using an algebraic method	2.3C, 2.3D, 2.3E, 3.6C	85–88, 172–175
NA3.04	calculate sides in right triangles, using the Pythagorean theorem, as required in topics throughout the course (e.g., measurement)	3.4A, 3.4B, 3.4C, 3.5B, 3.7B, 3.7D	150–153, 155, 190
NA3.05	substitute into measurement formulas and solve for one variable, with and without the help of technology	3.1A, 3.1B, 3.1C, 3.1D, 3.2A, 3.2B, 3.3B, 3.3C, 3.3D, 3.4B, 3.4C, 3.5B, 3.5C, 3.5D, 3.5F, 3.5G	130–135, 137–142, 145–149, 151–153, 155–158, 160–164

NA4.01	use algebraic modelling as one of several problem-solving strategies in various topics of the course (e.g., relations, measurement, direct and partial variation, the Pythagorean theorem, percent)	2.5A, 2.5B, 2.7E, 2.8A, 2.8B, 3.2A, 3.2B, 3.3A, 3.5F, 3.5G, 3.7A, 3.7B, 3.7C, 3.7D	97–104, 121–122, 123–128, 137–142, 143–144, 160–164, 189–192
NA4.02	compare algebraic modelling with other strategies used for solving the same problem	2.5A, 2.5B, 2.7E, 2.8A, 2.8B, 3.2A, 3.2B, 3.3A, 3.5F, 3.5G, 3.7A, 3.7B, 3.7C, 3.7D	97–104, 121–122, 123–128, 137–142, 143–144, 160, 189–192
NA4.03	communicate solutions to problems in appropriate mathematical forms (e.g., written explanations, formulas, charts, tables, graphs) and justify the reasoning used in solving the problems	2.5A, 2.5B, 2.7E, 2.8A, 2.8B, 3.2A, 3.2B, 3.3A, 3.5F, 3.5G, 3.7A, 3.7B, 3.7C, 3.7D, and throughout	97–104, 121–122, 123–128, 137–142, 143–144, 160–164, 189–192, and throughout

Strand: Relationships

Expectation Code	Specific Expectation	Student Resource Section/Activity	Student Resource Page Reference
RE1.02	demonstrate an understanding of some principles of sampling and surveying, and apply the principles in designing and carrying out experiments to investigate the relationships between variables	1.1A, 1.1B, 1.1C, 1.1D, 1.1E, 1.3B, 1.3C, 1.3D, 1.3E, 1.3F, 1.3E, 1.3F, 1.3G	
RE1.03	collect data using appropriate equipment and/or techniques	1.3B, 1.3C, 1.3D, 1.3E, 1.3F	32–41
RE1.04	organize and analyse data, using appropriate techniques and technology	1.1F, 1.3B, 1.3C, 1.3D, 1.3E, 1.3F, 3.3A, 3.6C	14–15, 32–41, 143–144, 172–175
RE1.05	describe trends and relationships observed in data, make inferences from data, compare the inferences with hypotheses about the data, and explain the differences between the inferences and the hypotheses	1.3B, 1.3C, 1.3D, 1.3E, 1.3F, 3.3A, 3.6C	32–41, 143–144, 172–175
RE1.06	communicate the findings of an experiment clearly and concisely, using appropriate mathematical forms (e.g., written explanations, formulas, charts, tables, graphs), and justify the conclusions reached	1.3B, 1.3C, 1.3D, 1.3E, 1.3F, 1.5A, 1.5B, 1.5C, 1.5D, 1.5E	32–41, 49–57
RE1.07	solve and/or pose problems related to an experiment, using the findings of the experiment	1.3B, 1.3C, 1.3D, 1.3E, 1.3F	32–41
RE2.01	construct tables of values, graphs, and formulas to represent linear relations derived from descriptions of realistic situations involving direct and partial variation (e.g., the cost of holding a banquet in a rented hall is $25 per person plus $975 for the hall)	1.3A, 1.3B, 1.3C, 1.3D, 2.5A, 2.8A, 2.8B	31–38, 97–100, 123–126
RE2.02	construct tables of values and scatter plots for linearly related data involving direct variation collected from experiments (e.g., the rebound height of a ball versus the height from which it was dropped)	1.3A, 1.3B, 1.3C, 1.3D, 2.5A, 2.8A, 2.8B	31–38, 97–100, 123–126
RE2.03	determine the equation of a line of best fit for a scatter plot, using an informal process (e.g., a process of trial and error on a graphing calculator; calculation of the equation of the line joining two carefully chosen points on the scatter plot	2.5A, 2.8A, 2.8B	97–100, 123–126

RE2.04	construct tables of values and graphs to represent non-linear relations derived from descriptions of realistic situations (e.g., represent the relationship between the volume of a cube and its side length, as the side length varies)	1.3A, 1.3B, 1.3C, 1.3D	31–38
RE2.05	demonstrate an understanding that straight lines represent linear relations and curves represent non-linear relations	1.3A, 1.3B, 1.3C, 1.3D, 1.4A, 1.4B, 1.4C, 2.5A, 2.8A, 2.8B	31–38, 42–48, 97–100, 123–126
RE3.01	determine values of a linear relation by using the formula of the relation and by interpolating or extrapolating from the graph of the relation (e.g., if a student earns $5/h caring for children, determine how long he or she must work to earn $143)	2.5A, 2.5B, 2.8A, 2.8B	97–104, 123–126
RE3.02	describe, in written form, a situation that would explain the events illustrated by a given graph of a relationship between two variables (e.g., write a story that matches the events shown in the graph)	1.5A, 1.5B, 1.5C, 1.5D, 1.5E	49–57
RE3.03	identify, by calculating finite differences in its table of values, whether a relation is linear or non-linear	1.4A, 1.4B, 1.4C, 1.5A, 1.6B	42–50, 60–61
RE3.04	describe the effect on the graph and the formula of a relation of varying the conditions of a situation they represent (e.g., if a graph showing partial variation represents the cost of producing a yearbook, describe how the appearance of the graph changes if the cost per book is altered; describe how it changes if the fixed costs are altered)	2.5A, 2.8A, 2.8B	97–100, 123–126

Strand: Analytic Geometry

Expectation Code	Specific Expectation	Student Resource Section/Activity	Student Resource Page Reference
AG1.01	determine, through investigations, the characteristics that distinguish the equation of a straight line from the equations of non-linear relations (e.g., use graphing software to obtain the graphs of a variety of linear and non-linear relations from their equations; classify the relations according to the shapes of their graphs; focus on the characteristics of the equations of linear relations and how they differ from the characteristics of the equations of non-linear relations)	2.7A	106–114
AG1.02	select the equations of straight lines from a given set of equations of linear and non-linear relations	2.7A	106–114
AG1.03	identify $y = mx + b$ as a standard form for the equation of a straight line, including the special cases $x = a$, $y = b$	2.7B, 2.7C, 3.3A, 3.6C, 3.7A, 3.7B, 3.7C, 3.7D	115–117, 143–144, 172–175, 189–192
AG2.01	identify practical situations illustrating slope (e.g., ramps, slides, staircases) and calculate the slopes of the inclines	1.6B, 2.4A, 2.4B, 2.4C, 2.4D, 3.3A, 3.6C	6061, 89–96, 143–144, 172–175
AG2.02	determine the slope of a line segment, using the formula $m = rise/run$	2.4A, 2.4B, 2.4C, 2.4D, 3.3A, 3.6C	89–96, 143–144, 172–175
AG2.03	identify the geometric significance of m and b in the equation $y = mx + b$ through investigation	2.5A, 2.5B, 2.7A, 2.7B, 2.7C, 2.7D, 2.7E, 2.7F, 2.8A, 2.8B, 3.3A, 3.6C	97–104, 106–128, 143–144, 172–174

AG2.04	identify the properties of the slopes of line segments (i.e., direction, positive or negative, rate of change, steepness, parallelism, perpendicularity) through investigations, facilitated by graphing technology where appropriate	1.6B, 2.5A, 2.5B, 2.7A, 2.7B, 2.7C, 2.7D, 2.7E, 2.7F, 3.3A, 3.6C	60–61, 97–104, 106–128, 172–174
AG3.01	plot points on the *xy*-plane and use the terminology and notation of the *xy*-plane correctly	2.6, 2.7F, 3.3A, 3.6C	105, 121–122, 143–144, 172–174
AG3.02	graph lines by hand, using a variety of techniques (e.g., making a table of values, using intercepts, using the slope and *y*-intercept)	2.7E, 2.7F, 3.3A, 3.7C, 3.7D	119–122, 143–144, 172–174, 191–192
AG3.03	graph lines, using graphing calculators or graphing software	2.7A, 3.7C, 3.7D	106–114, 191–192
AG3.04	determine the equation of a line, given the slope and *y*-intercept, the slope and a point on the line, and two points on the line	2.5A, 2.5B, 2.7B, 2.7C, 2.7D, 2.7E, 3.3A, 3.6C, 3.7C, 3.7D	97–104, 115–120, 143–144, 172–174, 191–192
AG3.05	communicate solutions in established mathematical form, with clear reasons given for the steps taken	2.5A, 2.8A, 2.8B, 3.3A, 3.6C, and throughout	97–104, 123–128, 143–144, 172–174, and throughout

Strand: Measurement and Geometry

Expectation Code	Specific Expectation	Student Resource Section/Activity	Student Resource Page Reference
MG1.01	construct a variety of rectangles for a given perimeter and determine the maximum area for a given perimeter	3.2A, 3.2B	137–142
MG1.02	construct a variety of square-based prisms for a given volume, and determine the minimum surface area for a square-based prism with a given volume	3.5F	160–162
MG1.03	construct a variety of cylinders for a given volume, and determine the minimum surface area for a cylinder with a given volume	3.5G	163–164
MG1.04	describe applications in which it would be important to know the maximum area for a given perimeter or the minimum surface area for a given volume (e.g., building a fence, designing a container)	3.2A, 3.2B, 3.5F	137–142, 160–162
MG2.01	solve problems involving the area of composite plane figures (e.g., combinations of rectangles, triangles, parallelograms, trapezoids, and circles)	3.1A, 3.1B, 3.1C, 3.1D, 3.1E, 3.3B, 3.3D	129–136, 145–147, 149
MG2.02	solve simple problems, using the formulas for the surface area of prisms and cylinders and for the volume of prisms, cylinders, cones, and spheres	3.5A, 3.5B, 3.5C, 3.5D, 3.5E, 3.5F, 3.5G	154–164
MG2.03	solve problems involving perimeter, area, surface area, volume, capacity in applications	3.1A, 3.1B, 3.1C, 3.1D, 3.1E, 3.2A, 3.2B, 3.3B, 3.3D, 3.5A, 3.5B, 3.5C, 3.5D, 3.5E, 3.5F, 3.5G	129–142, 145–147, 149, 154–164
MG2.04	judge the reasonableness of answers to measurement problems by considering likely results within the situation described in the problem	3.1D, 3.2A, 3.2B, 3.5G, and throughout	133–135, 137–142, 163–164, and throughout
MG2.05	judge the reasonableness of answers produced by a calculator, a computer, or pencil and paper, using mental mathematics and estimation	3.5E, 3.5G, and throughout	159, 163–164, and throughout
MG3.01	illustrate and explain the properties of the interior and exterior angles of triangles and quadrilaterals, and of angles related to parallel lines	3.6B, 3.6C, 3.6D, 3.6E, 3.6F, 3.6G	170–184

MG3.02	determine the properties of angle bisectors, medians, and altitudes in various types of triangles through investigation	3.6H, 3.6I	185–188
MG3.03	determine some properties of the sides and the diagonals of quadrilaterals (e.g., the diagonals of a rectangle bisect each other)	3.6G	183–184
MG3.04	communicate the findings of investigations, using appropriate language and mathematical forms (e.g., written explanations, diagrams, formulas, tables)	3.6B, 3.6C, 3.6D, 3.6E, 3.6F, 3.6G, 3.6H, 3.6I, 3.2A, 3.2B, 3.3A, 3.7B	137–144, 170–181, 183–188, 190

Pre-Planning Table

Unit 1: Relationships in Mathematics

Section	Activity	Specific Expectations	Suggested Timing	Materials (TRM = Teacher Resource Master)	Assessment Masters	Related Resources From *MATHPOWER*™ *9, Ontario Edition Blackline Masters*
1.1 Data Collection and Analysis	1.1A Data Collection 1.1B Using Surveys to Gather Data 1.1C Survey Assignment	RE1.03, RE1.04, RE1.05, RE1.06, NA1.03, NA4.03	150 min	• protractors • overhead projector	• 1 • 2	2.6, 2.7, 2.8, 4.1, 4.2, 4.3, 4.5, 4.8
	1.1D Learning Styles Inventory: Personal Results 1.1E Learning Styles Inventory: Class Results	RE1.03, RE1.04, RE1.05, RE1.06, NA1.03, NA4.03	150 min	• TRM 1 • protractors • overhead projector • unusual kitchen tools or other tools		
	1.1F Drawing a Histogram or Bar Graph on the TI-83 Plus	RE1.04	75 min	• TI-83 Plus graphing calculators • poster of graphing calculator • graphing calculator connected to an overhead projector • overhead projector		
1.2 Scatter Plots to Show Relationships	1.2A What Is a Scatter Plot?	RE2.02	75 min	• protractors • overhead projector		
	1.2B Positive, Negative, or No Correlation		75 min	• straight edges • overhead projector		
	1.2C Drawing the Line of Best Fit, 1.2D Practice: Scatter Plots and Lines of Best Fit 1.2E Describing Relationships	RE1.02, RE1.03, RE2.01, RE2.02, RE3.02	75 min	• straight edges • overhead projector	• 3	

1.3 Finding Relationships	1.3A The Hypothesis and the Conclusion 1.3B Cooling Temperature vs. Time 1.3C Can You Find a Relationship?	RE1.01, RE1.02, RE1.03, RE1.04, RE1.05, RE1.06, RE1.07, RE2.01, RE2.02, RE2.03, RE2.04	150 min	• straight edges, measuring tapes • overhead projector • hot drink in a mug • thermometer • large chart paper		
	1.3D Investigation: Finding Relationships	RE1.01, RE1.02, RE1.03, RE1.04, RE1.05, RE1.06, RE1.07, RE2.01, RE2.02, RE2.03, RE2.04, RE2.05	150–300 min	• TRMs 2 to 12 (8 copies of TRM 2 for each student) • large chart paper • markers • graphing calculators • overhead display screen		4.12
	1.3E Make an Experiment of Your Own	RE1.01, RE1.02, RE1.03, RE1.04, RE1.05, RE1.06, RE1.07	30 min each day for 2 days	• TRM 2 • materials needed by students for their own experiments	• 4	
	1.3F Summary Page and Journal	RE1.01, RE1.02, RE1.03, RE1.04, RE1.05, RE1.06, RE1.07	30 min			
1.4 Is It Really Linear?	1.4A Expressions Involving Integers 1.4B Relationships and First Differences 1.4C Practice: First Differences	NA1.02, RE3.03	150 min		• 5	1.6, 1.9
1.5 Combination Relationships	1.5A More Relationships	RE3.02, RE3.04	30 min	• overhead projector		4.9, 5.8
	1.5B A Picture Goes With the Story 1.5C Graphs That Represent a Story	RE3.02, RE3.04, AG1.01	50 min	• overhead projector		
	1.5D CBL™/CBR™ Data Collection and Graphs 1.5E Take a Walk and Tell the Story	RE3.04, AG1.02, AG3.03	150 min	• overhead projector • TI 83+ graphing calculators • CBR™ motion detectors	• 6	

1.6 Rates of Change	1.6A Estimate and Calculate Unit Rates	NA1.01, NA1.02	100 min	• containers of identical items but of different sizes	• 7	2.4
	1.6B Rates of Change	NA1.03, RE3.03, AG2.02, AG2.03	50 min	• 4 or more sets of circular objects that are exactly the same, with at least 6 in each set (e.g., CDs, buttons)		1.1
Final Assessment	Unit 1 Assessment Activities Unit 1 Assessment: Relationships and Graphing Journal Entry		225 min spread over 2–3 days		• 8 • 9 • 10 • 11	

Unit 2: Algebra and Relations

Section	Activity	Specific Expectations	Suggested Timing	Materials (TRM = Teacher Resource Master)	Assessment Masters	Related Resources From *MATHPOWER*™ *9, Ontario Edition Blackline Masters*
2.1 Exponents	2.1A Exponents: Introduction	NA2.01, NA2.05	75 min	• overhead projector • sheets of paper		
	2.1B Understanding Powers: Exponent Rules	NA2.01, NA2.06	150 min (with extra practice)		• 12	1.4, 1.5 1.7, 6.6, 6.7, 6.9
	2.1C Powers With Variables	NA2.02, NA2.06	50 min			
	2.1D The Negative Exponent: What Is It?	NA1.02, NA2.03	40 min	• overhead projector		3.2
	2.1E The Zero Exponent	NA2.03	20 min			
2.2 Scientific Notation and Exponents	2.2A Using Scientific Notation	NA1.02, NA1.04, NA2.03, NA2.04, NA2.05	150 min		• 13	3.1, 3.3
2.3 Algebra	2.3A Like Terms	NA1.02, NA3.01, NA3.02	150 min (including extra practice)	• overhead algebra tiles • algebra tiles		6.1, 6.3, 6.4
	2.3B How to Handle Brackets	NA1.02, NA3.01, NA3.02	150 min (including extra practice)	• algebra tiles		6.4, 6.5 Optional: 6.6, 6.8 (with caution)

2.3 Algebra	2.3C Solving Equations 2.3D Magic Equations: Magic Square	NA1.02, NA3.03	200 min (including additional practice)	• balance scale • overhead projector • overhead algebra tiles • the game *Hands-On Equations®*		7.1, 7.2, 7.3, 7.4, 7.5, 7.9
	2.3E Algebra: Practice	NA1.02, NA2.02, NA3.01, NA3.02, NA3.03	45 min			
2.4 Slopes	2.4A Slopes of Staircases and Ramps	NA1.03, AG2.01, AG2.02	75 min	• 1-cm interlocking cubes • large grid paper • overhead projector		2.1, 2.3 (ratios)
	2.4B Finding Slopes of Stairs	NA1.03, AG2.01, AG2.02	40 min		• 14	
	2.4C Finding Slopes of Ramps	NA1.03, AG2.01, AG2.02	20 min	• measuring tapes • boards • books		
	2.4D Assignment: Slopes of Stairs and Ramps	AG2.01, AG2.02, NA1.03	10 min review in class	• boards • books		
2.5 Linear Models	2.5A Modelling Linear Relationships	AG2.04, AG3.03, AG3.04, RE2.01, RE2.02, RE2.03, RE2.05, RE3.01, RE3.04, NA4.01, NA4.02, NA4.03	75 min	• overhead projector		5.3, 5.5 Use with caution. Partial and direct variation will need to be explained. Suggest finding other resources.
	2.5B Modelling Linear Relationships: Pair–Share	AG2.03, AG2.04, AG3.04, NA4.01, NA4.02, NA4.03, RE3.01	40 min	• overhead projector • large grid paper	• 15	
2.6 The Cartesian Plane		NA1.02, AG3.01	45 min	• overhead projector • large chart paper	• 16	1.10, 5.1, 5.2, 5.3

2.7 The Equation $y = mx + b$	2.7A Linear Equations $y = mx + b$ Using Graphing Technology	AG1.01, AG1.02, AG2.03, AG2.04, AG3.03	150 min	• graphing calculators • graphing software such as Graphmatica		5.6
	2.7B Lines and More Lines	AG1.03, AG2.03, AG2.04, AG3.04	75 min	• overhead projector	• 17	8.1, 8.3, 8.4 (Omit from Master 8.4 questions 5–8, and 19), 8.6
	2.7C Equations of Lines: Chart	AG1.03, AG2.03, AG2.04, AG3.04	40 min		• 18	5.4, 8.5 (Rearrange the equations in questions 5 and 6 into $y = mx + b$ form.)
	2.7D Find the Equation of a Line	NA4.01, NA4.02, NA4.03, AG2.03, AG2.04, AG3.02, AG3.04	100 min	• large grid paper • overhead projector • overhead grid	• 19	
	2.7E Find the Equation of a Line That Represents the Cost	NA4.01, NA4.02, NA4.03, AG2.03, AG2.04, AG3.02	55 min	• large overhead grid • large grid paper • overhead projector		8.2
	2.7F Graphing Lines: Three Methods	AG3.01, AG3.02	75 min	• large overhead grid • large grid paper • overhead projector		5.4, 8.5 (Rearrange equations 5 and 6 into $y = mx + b$ form.)
2.8 Linear Models for Comparison Shopping	2.8A Example of Comparison Shopping 2.8B Comparison Shopping: Practice	NA4.01, NA4.02, NA4.03, RE2.01, RE2.02, RE2.03, RE2.05, RE3.01, RE3.04, AG3.05, AG2.03	100 min	• TRM 13 (Comparison Shopping) • overhead projector • overhead grid • coloured pens	• 20	
Unit 2 Review			Five 30-min periods	• Review Masters 1–5		
Final Assessment	Unit 2 Relations and Algebra Unit 2 Final Assessment: Journal Entry		Five 40-min periods		• 21 • 22 • 23 • 24 • 25	

Unit 3: Relationships in Geometry

Section	Activity	Specific Expectations	Suggested Timing	Materials (TRM = Teacher Resource Master)	Assessment Masters	Related Resources From *MATHPOWER*™ *9, Ontario Edition Blackline Masters*
3.1 Area and Perimeter	3.1A Rectangles 3.1B Area and Perimeter: Class Activity 3.1C Area and Perimeter: Combined Shapes	NA3.05, MG2.01, MG2.03	75 min	• overhead projector		9.1 (Choose appropriate questions.)
	3.1D Area and Perimeter: Applications	NA3.05, MG2.01, MG2.03, MG2.04	75 min			2.8 (percent)
	3.1E Area Assignment: Redecorate a Room	MG2.01, MG2.03	15 min to review expectations		• 26	pages 68–70
3.2 Maximum Areas	3.2A A Swimmingly Great Problem	NA3.05, NA4.01, NA4.02, NA4.03, MG1.01, MG1.04, MG2.03, MG2.04	75 min	• overhead projector • large grid paper		
	3.2B Down the Garden Path: Maximum Area	NA3.05, NA4.01, NA4.02, NA4.03, MG1.01, MG1.04, MG2.03, MG2.04	75 min	• overhead projector • large grid paper		
3.3 Circles	3.3A Pi Development	NA4.01, NA4.02, NA4.03, AG1.03, RE1.04, RE1.05, AG2.01, AG2.02, AG2.03, AG2.04, AG3.01, AG3.02, AG3.04, AG3.05	45 min	• round objects of various sizes • measuring tapes • string • rulers		

3.3 Circles	3.3B Circle: Area and Circumference	NA2.02, NA3.05, MG2.01, MG2.03	75 min	• overhead projector	• 27	9.1 (Select)
	3.3C Areas of Combined Shapes	NA2.01, NA2.03, NA3.05	20 min		• 28	9.1 (Select)
	3.3D Round and Round and Round . . .	NA3.05, MG2.01, MG2.03	20 min			
3.4 Pythagorean Theorem	3.4A Pythagorean Theorem Puzzle	NA3.04	20 min	• TRM 14 (Pythagorean Theorem Puzzle) • glue sticks • scissors		
	3.4B Using the Pythagorean Theorem	NA3.04, NA3.05	50 min	• overhead projector		3.12 (Omit the formulas for 35. Just do the questions.), 7.8 (questions 9 and 10)
	3.4C More Pythagoras	NA3.04, NA3.05	20 min		• 29	
3.5 Three-Dimensional Geometry	3.5A Nets and Solids	MG2.02, MG2.03	30–60 min	• nets of three-dimensional solids		Blackline Masters 4.9, 5.8
	3.5B Surface Area of Prisms 3.5C Three-Dimensional Geometry: Surface Area	NA3.05, MG2.02, MG2.03	200 min	• TRM 15, Three-Dimensional Geometry Solids • nets of three-dimensional solids	• 30	
	3.5D Volume of a Prism	NA3.05, MG2.02, MG2.03	45 min plus practice time	• 10 equal-sized corrugated rectangles, triangles, and circles		9.2, 9.3, 9.4 (Select questions involving the volume of prisms.)
	3.5E Volume of a Pyramid	NA3.05, MG2.02, MG2.03, MG2.05	45 min	• hollow three-dimensional prisms and pyramids • pourable materials such as water, oatmeal, rice, and confetti	• 31	9.2, 9.3, 9.4 (Select questions involving the volume of pyramids.) .
	3.5F Minimum Surface Area: Rectangular Prism	NA3.03, NA4.01, NA4.02, NA4.03, MG1.02, MG1.04	75 min	• 1-cm interlocking cubes		pages 48–53 (Building a Better Box)

3.5 Three-Dimensional Geometry	3.5G Surface Area and Volume of a Cylinder	MG1.03, MG2.02, MG2.04, MG2.05, NA3.05, NA4.01, NA4.02, NA4.03	45 min	• sheets of paper • tape • a pourable material, such as popcorn		
3.6 Relations in Euclidean Geometry	3.6A Introduction to *The Geometer's Sketchpad®*		75–150 min	• *The Geometer's Sketchpad®* software • data projector hooked up to a computer	• 32	
	3.6B The Sum of the Angles of a Polygon	MG3.01, MG3.04, MG3.05	75 min	• *The Geometer's Sketchpad®* software		10.1 (Select)
	3.6C The Sum of the Interior Angles of a Polygon: Activity	MG3.01, MG3.04, MG3.05, AG1.03, RE1.04, RE1.05, AG2.01, AG2.02, AG2.03, AG2.04, AG3.01, AG3.02, AG3.04, AG3.05, NA3.03	75 min			10.1 (Select)
	3.6D Exterior Angles of a Polygon	MG3.01, MG3.04, MG3.05	75 min	• *The Geometer's Sketchpad®* software		10.1 (Select)
	3.6E Using Dynamic Geometry to "Prove" Geometric Theorems: Angles	MG3.01, MG3.04, MG3.05	45 min	• *The Geometer's Sketchpad®* software	• 33	10.1 (Select)
	3.6F Using Dynamic Geometry to "Prove" Geometric Theorems: Parallel Lines	MG3.01	45 min	• *The Geometer's Sketchpad®* software	• 34	10.1 (Select)

3.6 Relations in Euclidian Geometry	3.6G Using Dynamic Geometry to Look at Quadrilaterals	MG3.01, MG3.03, MG3.04, MG3.05	45+ min	• *The Geometer's Sketchpad®* software	• 35	
	3.6H Circumcentre of a Triangle 3.6I Triangle Centres and Their Properties	MG3.02, MG3.04, MG3.05	75 min	• *The Geometer's Sketchpad®* software • data projector		
3.7 Relations and *The Geometer's Sketchpad*Ò	3.7A Pi Demonstration (Again) 3.7B The Pythagorean Theorem Using *The Geometer's Sketchpad®* 3.7C Equations of Lines and *The Geometer's Sketchpad®* 3.7D Family of Lines: Activity	NA3.04, NA4.01, NA4.02, NA4.03, AG1.03	150 min	• *The Geometer's Sketchpad®* software		
Sketchpad Assessment			75 min		• *The Geometer's Sketchpad®* software	• 37
Final Assessment	Unit 3 Assessment Activities Unit 3 Assessment: Relationships and Graphing Journal Entry		225 min spread over 2–3 days		• 36 • 37	

Acknowledgements

We acknowledge the support, ideas, and enthusiasm of all the people who have, directly or indirectly, contributed to creating the student resource, *Mathematics 9: Exploring the Concepts*, and the corresponding Teacher's Resource. We thank our colleagues, friends, and family who encouraged us to write the student resource for the benefit of the students. Joseph Stein and John Dallan, by their commitment to the profession and personal leadership, created a nurturing environment for us to become successful teachers. Their mentorship contributed to the confidence necessary to commence this project.

This book is a result of our personal experiences and efforts, combined with the thoughts and inspirations of others. We also thank our publisher, Diane Wyman, for her continued guidance from the beginning.

Finally, we thank our students for providing the incentive to initiate this venture.

Anne and Rod

Unit 1 Teaching Notes

Section 1.1 Data Collection and Analysis

1.1A Data Collection

1.1B Using Surveys to Gather Data

1.1C Survey Assignment

Student Resource pp. 2–7

Warm Up
Review percents, ratios, and drawing bar graphs and circle graphs. Remind the students about the need to title the graph and label and scale the axes.

Teaching Suggestions
In Activity 1.1A, discuss with the class the questions given on student resource page 2. Point out that a **hypothesis** is a statement of what you think the outcome will be, and that, once you have collected the data, you can then adjust or correct the hypothesis to make a conclusion. The conclusion is a statement of the actual outcome.

Activity 1.1B introduces the terms **census survey**, **sample survey**, and **random sample**. This activity provides the students with an opportunity to model survey taking and analysis (ice cream). Have volunteers present their answers, and put the results of the data collection on an overhead projector transparency. Demonstrate, using an overhead projector and input from the students, how to use the data to complete all the types of graphs: bar, line, and circle.

In Activity 1.1C, pairs of students are asked to make up their own survey, collect and organize the data, display and analyse the data, and finally make a conclusion. These are all the required steps when dealing with statistics. Have volunteers present their results to the class.

Common Errors
Check that, when the students are making up survey questions, their questions are appropriate.

Assessment
Distribute *Assessment Master 1*, A1.1C Rubric for Survey: Assignment, and review your expectations and the rubric. Then distribute *Assessment Master 2*, Survey: Quiz, and have pairs of students complete it. Have pairs come to the front of the class in turn to do their survey with their classmates. Have the students present their results to the class, using large grid paper, overhead projector, etc., for a communication mark. This could be done over several days. Mark it for formative quiz and for summative assessment.

> "A statistician is someone who can put his hand in the oven and his feet in the freezer and tell you, 'On average, I feel just fine.' "
>
> Anonymous

Specific Expectations
RE1.03, RE1.04, RE1.05, RE1.06, NA 1.03, NA4.03

Overall Goals and Key Concepts
- collect data
- introduce terminology
- display survey data
- analyse survey data

Materials
- *Assessment Master 1*, A1.1C Rubric for Survey: Assignment
- *Assessment Master 2*, A1.1C Survey: Assignment
- overhead projector
- large grid paper

Timing
150 min

Related Resources
MATHPOWER™ 9, Ontario Edition, Blackline Masters Masters 2.6, 2.7, 2.8, 4.1, 4.2, 4.3, 4.5, 4.6, 4.8

Specific Expectations
RE1.03, RE1.04, RE1.05, RE1.06, NA1.03, NA4.03

Overall Goals and Key Concepts
- complete a survey
- introduce the term hypothesis
- display survey data
- analyse survey data

Materials
- *Teacher Resource Master 1,* Learning Styles Inventory
- protractors
- overhead projector
- unusual tools and kitchen apparatus
- chart paper

Timing
150 min

1.1D Learning Styles Inventory: Personal Results

1.1E Learning Styles Inventory: Class Results

Student Resource pp. 8–13

Warm Up

Discuss learning styles by bringing into class unusual tools/ kitchen apparatus. Ask the students how they would best learn to use these: by watching someone use them, by trying them, or by having their use explained to them. Briefly explain the term **hypothesis**. Have the students "hypothesize" about which learning style they think they follow.

Teaching Suggestions

In Activity 1.1D, provide the students with the *Teacher Resource Master 3,* Learning Styles Inventory, and explain how to complete it. Point out that there are no right or wrong answers. Have the students complete the inventory, and then complete questions 1 to 5 on student resource page 8. Finally, assign the questions on pages 9 and 10 as seatwork and/or homework.

In Activity 1.1E, collect class data on a chalkboard or chart paper. Have the students complete the activity.

Take time to talk to the students about their learning styles, and how they affect their day-to-day life. *Teacher Resource Master 1,* Learning Styles Inventory, includes some analysis of different learning styles that may be helpful in discussion.

Specific Expectations
RE1.04

Overall Goals and Key Concepts
- display data on a graphing calculator

Materials
- T1-83 graphing calculators
- poster of graphing calculator
- graphing calculator connected to an overhead projector
- overhead projector

1.1F Drawing a Histogram or Bar Graph on the TI-83 Plus

Student Resource pp. 14–15

Warm Up

Provide the students, or pairs of students, with graphing calculators, Allow the students some time (10 minutes) for structured play using the graphing calculator. They need to try it, hear the instructions for using it, and see how it works.

Teaching Suggestions

Using a graphing calculator connected to an overhead projector or a poster of a graphing calculator, demonstrate, step by step, what keys to press and what the screen should look like. An overhead display unit is invaluable for a demonstration such as this. Have the students use the graphing calculators to redo their graphs from previous activities' histograms. Discuss the advantages and disadvantages of this method of displaying data (colour, size, ease, precision, ease of making changes, etc.)

Section 1.2 Scatter Plots to Show Relationships

1.2A What Is a Scatter Plot?

Student Resource pp. 16–19

Specific Expectations

RE2.02

Overall Goals and Key Concepts

- understand the terms **independent variable** and **dependent variable**

Materials

- protractors
- overhead projector

Timing

75 min

Warm Up

Introduce and review the term **scatter plot**. If review of scaling graphs is necessary, discuss the appropriateness of scale choice, and point out that there can be more than one correct choice of scale.

Teaching Suggestions

While the students are reading the page, place the page on an overhead projector. Introduce the terms **independent variable**, **dependent variable**, **continuous data**, and **discrete data**.

Have small groups of students create two different sets of data, one involving discrete data and one involving continuous data. Then, have the groups share their results with the class. Use these examples to discuss which variable is the dependent variable and which is the independent variable.

Common Errors

Some students have difficulty distinguishing between the independent variable and the dependent variable. Point out that the independent variable is in the left column of the table of values, and is plotted along the horizontal axis, and the dependent variable is in the right column of the table of values, and is plotted along the vertical axis.

1.2B Positive, Negative, or No Correlation?

Student Resource pp. 20–23

Specific Expectations

RE2.02, RE3.02

Overall Goals and Key Concepts

- understand the concept of positive, negative, and no correlation

Materials

- straightedges
- overhead projector

Timing

75 min

Warm Up

Explain to the students that a positive correlation can be represented by a line going upward from left to right, a negative correlation by a line going downward from left to right.

Teaching Suggestions

Students need straightedges, preferably clear ones, so that they can see their dots through them. Demonstrate how to use the clear straightedge. Do the examples with the students on an overhead projector. When labelling the axes, review the meaning of the terms **independent variable**, **dependent variable**, **continuous data**, and **discrete data**. As a class, have the students create and share examples of positive, negative, and no correlation.

Gradually introduce and use the terms used to describe a good hypothesis, in preparation for Section 1.3. Continue this throughout Section 1.2.

1.2C Drawing the Line of Best Fit

1.2D Practice: Scatter Plots and Lines of Best Fit

1.2E Describing Relationships

Student Resource pp. 24–30

Warm Up

Review with the students the terms from the previous lesson, i.e., independent variable, dependent variable, continuous data, discrete data, and positive correlation, negative correlation, and no correlation.

Teaching Suggestions

Demonstrate to the students how using a clear straightedge helps them to see clearly the dots on their graph, and thus makes the drawing of the line of best fit more accurate.

Do the examples with the students on an overhead projector. Point out to the students that a line of best fit is an estimated line, and thus, there can be many lines of best fit for the same set of data. Demonstrate and discuss other lines of best fit, and why one might be better than another. Discuss points that are **outliers**. These are points that are widely separated from the rest of the points in the graph, and often represent a value that is out of the expected range of values.

Review the terms **interpolation** and **extrapolation**. Have the students practise finding values using both these methods.

In Activity 1.2E, briefly introduce the idea of curve of best fit. Use parts d) and e) to demonstrate this concept.

Assessment

Distribute *Assessment Master 3*, A1.2D Line of Best Fit: Quiz, and have the students complete it. Collect and mark it for formative assessment.

Section 1.3 Finding Relationships

1.3A The Hypothesis and the Conclusion,

1.3B Cooling Temperature vs. Time,

1.3C Can You Find a Relationship?

Student Resource pp. 31–37

Warm Up

Review with the class the term **hypothesis**.

Teaching Suggestions

In Activity 1.3A, the process of making a hypothesis is formalized. Describe to the class the five questions that need to be answered in making a hypothesis. Write these five questions on chart paper, and display the chart in a prominent place in the class for student reference. Discussion will be required for (0, 0) as a point. Knowing whether the point (0, 0) is a member of the data indicates

---

Specific Expectations

RE1.02, RE1.03, RE2.01

Overall Goals and Key Concepts

- draw the line of best fit
- use the language of relationships correctly

Materials

- *Assessment Master 3*, A1.2D Line of Best Fit: Quiz
- clear straightedges
- overhead projector

Timing

75 min

"Acknowledge, encourage and praise sincere effort."
Harvey Silver and Bart Mindszenthy

Specific Expectations

RE1.01, RE1.02, RE1.03, RE1.04, RE1.05, RE1.06, RE1.07, RE2.01, RE2.02, RE2.04, RE2.05

Overall Goals and Key Concepts

- gather data for 2-variable relationships
- make hypotheses, then, make conclusions

Materials

- large chart paper
- thermometer

Materials – *continued*

- hot drink in a mug
- measuring tapes
- rulers
- overhead projector
- straight edges

Timing

150 min

Related Resources

MATHPOWER™ 9,
Ontario Edition,
Blackline Masters
Masters 4.12

Specific Expectations

RE1.01, RE1.02, RE1.03,
RE1.04, RE1.05, RE1.06,
RE1.07, RE2.01, RE2.02,
RE2.03, RE2.04, RE2.05

Overall Goals and Key Concepts

- make hypotheses (predictions)
- investigation by experiment, data collection and graph
- make conclusions

Materials

- *Teacher Resource Master 2* (Experiment Sheet), 8 copies per student, one per experiment
- *Teacher Resource Master 3* (Experiment Marking Checklist)
- *Teacher Resource Master 4 to 12* (Experiments)
- large chart paper
- markers
- graphing calculators
- overhead display screen

Timing

150–300 min

whether the relationship represents a direct variation or a partial variation. Have the students highlight important parts of Activity 1.3A of their student resource.

Activities 1.3A and 1.3B can be completed at the same time. For Activity 1.3B, show the class how to use the experiment sheet, by modelling the experiment in front of the class. For this you will need a hot drink in a mug, and a thermometer. Draw a large table of values (temperature vs. time). Assign a pair of students to collect the data every 5 min over a 40- to 60-min time period. As the liquid is cooling and the students are collecting the data, have the students come up with the answers to the five questions needed to make the hypothesis for the temperature of the drink vs. time. When you have completed the experiment, including the scatter plot and the curve of best fit, have the students review the hypothesis, make adjustments to it, and, then, state a conclusion.

In Activity 1.3C, provide pairs of students with measuring tapes and rulers. Have them collect each other's data and record it on a data sheet on an overhead projector transparency. All students record the data collected on their own data sheets given on student resource page 33. The students will then use these data to complete the activity.

1.3D Investigation: Finding Relationships

Student Resource p. 38

Warm Up

Display the experiment sheet in Activity 1.3D on an overhead projector and discuss your expectations of its use. This is a good time to review the five points of the hypothesis. Students could use this page in their student resource to once again describe what each point represents. Instruct the students to ignore the third column of the table of values for now. It will be used to record first differences later, when determining linearity.

Teaching Suggestions

For Activity 1.3D, set up four stations in the classroom. On the first day, supply each station with appropriate equipment and one set of written instructions for the experiments involving linear relationships in the *Teacher Resource Masters 4 to 8*. The materials and the methods for each experiment are given in the table on the following page.

Demonstrate to the class how to do each experiment. It will not be adequate for them to read the instructions and then do the experiment. In small groups, have the students circulate to gather data at each station. It may be necessary to collect some data before making the hypothesis. Once they have collected the data, have them draw the scatter plot and answer questions on the experiment sheet independently. Circulate to check that the students are correctly identifying, independent and dependent variables, that they are choosing the appropriate scales, and that they are including all parts of the hypothesis.

Several days later do the same with the non-linear and no relationship (no correlation) experiments in the *Teacher Resource Masters 9 to 12*.

Assign each group an experiment for them to present to the class. Provide large chart paper and markers, or have them plot scatter plots on graphing calculators. Display the results in the classroom. Reflect on the experiments completed on day 1 before beginning the experiments on day 2. Remind the students to keep each of their experiment sheets, as they will need to complete them at a later date.

Related Resources

*MATHPOWER™ 9,
Ontario Edition,
Blackline Masters*
Master 4.12

Assessment

Allow the class time to prepare and practise their presentation. Give a communication mark on the presentation. As the presentations are being made, the students in the class can make any necessary corrections to their experiment sheets. Collect and mark all experiment write ups using *Teacher Resource Master 3*, Experiment Marking Checklist, provided.

Materials required, and detailed instructions and conclusions for the various experiments in Activity 1.3D Investigation: Finding Relationships.

Experiment	Materials Required	Experiment Instructions
Height of Object vs. Length of Shadow (*Teacher Resource Master 4*)	• at least 6 objects ranging in height from 5 cm to 30 cm • lamp with 100 W bulb • white paper and tape	Find a spot in the classroom where a shadow will show. Put white paper on this surface to enhance the shadow. Plug in the lamp and shine it toward the white surface. Put tape on the surface, so that each object is placed consistently. The relationship is linear with positive correlation.
Mass vs. Distance of Bag From Floor (*Teacher Resource Master 5*)	• shopping bag with several strong long rubber bands looped through the handle • metre stick • at least 5 of the same items of significant mass (this student resource will do)	Hang the bag from the rubber bands so that the bottom of the bag is about 1 m from the floor. Add books, one at a time, recording the distance of the bottom of the bag from the floor each time. The relationship is linear with negative correlation.
Mass vs. Number of Books (*Teacher Resource Master 6*)	• scales • at least 8 books of the same mass	The students place a book on the scale and record the mass. The students then increase the number of books on the scale by one, and record the total mass of the books after each addition. The relationship is linear with positive correlation.
Pendulum Length vs. Time (*Teacher Resource Master 7*)	• a piece of string, 1 m long, with marks at the 40-cm length, 50 cm length, 60-cm length, etc. (The string can be knotted at these places.) • mass on end of string so it will swing freely • stopwatch	One student will hold the string at the 30-cm mark. One student will pull the pendulum out to the required angle, and let it swing freely. A second student will time how long the pendulum takes to make five complete swings. For the next trial, the pendulum is held at the next mark, and the swinging and recording are repeated. And so on. The length of the pendulum is plotted against the corresponding time for five swings. The relationship is linear and positive.
Pendulum Mass vs. Time (*Teacher Resource Master 8*)	• pendulum (string will do) • a variety of masses that can be added at equal increments (heavy duty paper clips work well and can be easily added to the end of the string. Washers also work well, but require a hook on the end of the string.)	One student adds a mass to the end of the pendulum. Another student pulls the string out to the required angle, and then lets it swing freely. A third student times how long it takes to make five complete swings. The number of masses at the end of the pendulum is increased by 1, and the next reading is taken. And so on. The relationship is linear and constant.
Height vs. Diameter (*Teacher Resource Master 9*)	• at least 8 cylinders of different heights and diameters. The more variety, the better. • measuring tapes	Students measure and record the height and the diameter of the cylinders and graph the recordings. No relationship (no correlation). This sometimes surprises the students.

Pieces of Chocolate Bar Remaining vs. Number of Bites (*Teacher Resource Master 10*)	• the second page of *Teacher Resource Master 10* containing the chocolate bar divided into pieces for each group • alternatively, a bag containing 32 pieces of candy, where half of the candies are removed at each pass	The students pass the chocolate bar sheet around the group. Each student removes half of the pieces of chocolate bar. The students graph the number of passes vs. the number of pieces of chocolate bar remaining. The relationship is non-linear (exponential) with negative correlation.
Area vs. Length of the Side of a Square (*Teacher Resource Master 11*)	• 1-cm grid paper (*Teacher Resource Master 14*) • 1-cm interlocking cubes	The students draw, or build, a square of side length 1 cm, and find the area. They only need to count squares if they forget the area formula. Repeat the step above for squares of side length 2 cm, 3 cm, 4 cm, etc. Graph the side length vs. area. The relationship is non-linear (exponential) with positive correlation.
Volume vs. Length of the Side of a Cube (*Teacher Resource Master 12*)	• 1-cm interlocking cubes (The students can pre-make the cubes with 1-cm interlocking cubes, so that the cubes do not have to be made each time.)	The students select from the pre-made cubes. They find the volume of cubes of side length 1 cm, 2 cm, 3 cm, etc. It may be necessary for them to dismantle the cubes in order to count the 1 cm interlocking cubes for the volume. Graph side length vs. volume. The relationship is non-linear (exponential) with positive correlation.

1.3E Make an Experiment of Your Own

Student Resource pp. 39–40

Warm Up

Discuss with the class the choices for an experiment provided in Activity 1.3D. Discuss other options for experiments.

Teaching Suggestions

The students can work in small groups of 2 to 4 to plan and implement their own experiment. In the first day, have the students do Steps A to D. Circulate to be sure the students describe their experiment accurately. Have the students provide you with a list of materials they require to carry out their experiment, so that these materials are ready for them the next day. Provide the groups with some class time the next day to perform their experiment and collect the data and make conclusions. The students could present their results to the class, or you could collect the results and mark for formative assessment.

Assessment

Distribute *Assessment Master 4*, A1.3E Two-Variable Relationships and Lines of Best Fit: Quiz, and have the students complete it. Collect and mark it for formative assessment.

Specific Expectations
RE1.01, RE1.02, RE1.03, RE1.04, RE1.05, RE1.06, RE1.07

Overall Goals and Key Concepts
• use knowledge and skills learned from experiments to design and implement an experiment
• make hypotheses (predictions)
• collect and present data
• make conclusions

Materials
• *Teacher Resource Master 2*, (Experiment Sheet)
• *Assessment Master 4*, A1.3E Two-Variable Relationships and Lines of Best Fit: Quiz
• materials needed by students for their own experiments

Timing
30 min each day, for 2 days

Specific Expectations
RE1.01, RE1.02, RE1.03,
RE1.04, RE1.05, RE1.06,
RE1.07

Overall Goals and Key
Concepts
• use correct mathematical
  language to articulate the
  vocabulary in this unit

Materials
• *Teacher Resource Master
  13* (Journal Entry)

Timing
30 min

Specific Expectations
NA10.2, RE2.05, RE3.03

Overall Goals and Key
Concepts
• find first differences
• determine the linearity of
  a relationship

Timing
150 min

Related Resources
*MATHPOWER™ 9,
Ontario Edition,
Blackline Masters*
Masters 1.6, 1.9

"To climb steep hills
requires slow pace at first."
William
Shakespeare

1.3F Summary Page and Journal

Student Resource p. 41

Teaching Suggestions

Provide the students with *Teacher Resource Masters 13* (Journal Entry), and suggest that they complete this master in pencil, so that corrections can be made to it. Do this activity along with Activity 1.3E, Make an Experiment of Your Own. The students can refer to their notes, if necessary. Have the students proofread each other's work. Encourage those students who have difficulty with written language to do this activity on a word processor, and cut and paste their answers into their student resource.

Section 1.4 Is It Really Linear?

1.4A Expressions Involving Integers

1.4B Relationships and First Differences

1.4C Practice: First Differences

Student Resource pp. 42–48

Warm Up

Activity 1.4A provides a review of integer operations that the students may need before doing first differences. The students usually find it easier to review multiplication and division first. When doing addition and subtraction, reduce adjacent signs to a single sign using multiplication rules. Add and subtract integers by going up and down the thermometer provided on student resource pages 43 and 44.

Teaching Suggestions

In Activity 1.4B, the students should be able to make a perfect hypothesis for this example. Explain first differences to the students and how to find them. Have pairs of students complete the data and graph and make observations. Give the students time to find their investigations and experiment sheets and identify those where the independent variable increases by equal increments (pendulum-2, mass of books-2, area, volume, chocolate bar). Now, tell the students to complete the third column with the first differences. Make observations with the class, noting that all linear relations have a constant for the first difference. Assign student resource pages 46–48 for homework. Have the students include write ups similar to those shown in the first example. Point out that in some of the later sets of data, some of the numbers are intentionally skipped.

Common Errors

The independent variable must increase by equal increments. In the experiments, the first differences may not always be **exact** due to human error.

Assessment

Distribute *Assessment Master 5*, A1.4C First Differences: Quiz, and have the students complete it. Collect and mark it for formative assessment.

Section 1.5 Combination Relationships

1.5A More Relationships

Student Resource pp. 49–50

Warm Up
Review the terms **positive correlation** and **negative correlation**.

Teaching Suggestions
Have the students fill in the definitions at the top half of student resource page 49. Illustrate the different relationships by showing a few examples on the overhead projector. Have the students show and explain their answers to the class. Point out that there can be more than one correct answer. The students often enjoy sharing their own examples and answers. As the activity progresses, encourage different students to present.

1.5B A Picture Goes With the Story

1.5C Graphs That Represent a Story

Student Resource pp. 51–52

Teaching Suggestions
For Activity 1.5B, with the class, make up a few examples similar to those on the page. Give pairs of students an opportunity to draw a graph of their own trip to school. Then, use the overhead projector to review each graph. Discuss the different possible graphs for the last example. Talk about how a particular graph would change if the person slowed down, stopped, or sped up. Assign Activity 1.5C as homework.

Specific Expectations
RE1.06, RE3.02, RE3.04

Overall Goals and Key Concepts
• recognize that a relationship can be a combination of several relationships

Materials
• overhead projector

Timing
30 min

Related Resources
MATHPOWER™ 9, Ontario Edition, Blackline Masters
Masters 4.9, 5.8

Specific Expectations
RE1.06, RE3.02, RE3.04, AG1.01

Overall Goals and Key Concepts
• interpret graphs
• prepare for CBR™ activity

Materials
• overhead projector

Timing
50 min

Specific Expectations
RE1.06, RE3.02, RE3.04,
AG1.02

Overall Goals and Key
Concepts
- understand how a graph
  relates to distance, speed,
  and time

Materials
- *Assessment Master 6,
  A1.5E Story Time and
  Take a Walk: Quiz*
- overhead projector
- graphing calculators
- CBR™ motion detectors

Timing
150 min

"The teacher is responsible
for the climate in the
classroom."
    T. Anne and Rod Yeager

1.5D CBL™/CBR™ Data Collection and Graphs

1.5E Take a Walk and Tell the Story

Student Resource pp. 53–57

Warm Up
Discuss how speed, time, and distance are related in terms of correlation and
steepness of graph.

Teaching Suggestions
Attach a graphing calculator to an overhead projector. Use the Ranger
Program/Match a Graph. Use the CBR™ motion detector to track motion.
Demonstrate how to match the graph and, then, ask as many volunteers as
possible to match a graph. Give the volunteers a second chance if they feel that
they can improve upon their first trial.

Distribute a graphing calculator and a CBR™ motion detector to each pair
of students in the class. Review Activity 1.5D, which demonstrates how to use
the Ranger Program.

Introduce Activity 1.5E by explaining that every pair of students will be
doing this activity. This activity will involve walking toward a wall and taking
readings on the CBR™ motion detector. Have the students *hold* the CBR™
and the calculator and practise walking toward a wall. You may find it
necessary to rearrange your classroom or to use a hall or the gym. Choose a
spot with minimum interference.

Common Errors
In Part A, the students are to draw their guess of the graph before doing the
walking. Check with their partners for agreement on graphs before they begin
the CBR™ activity. In Part B, the students are to write the story before doing
the walking. This exercise is worth the chaos.

Assessment
Distribute *Assessment Master 6*, A1.5E Story Time and Take a Walk: Quiz, and
have the students complete it. Collect and mark it for formative assessment.

Section 1.6 Rates of Change

1.6A Estimate and Calculate Unit Rates

Student Resource pp. 58–59

Specific Expectations

NA1.01, NA1.02, NA1.03, NA1.06

Overall Goals and Key Concepts

- estimate and calculate unit rates

Materials

- *Assessment Master 7, A1.6A Estimate the Unit Cost: Quiz*
- can, bottles, containers of identical items but of different sizes

Timing

100 min

Related Resources

MATHPOWER™ 9, Ontario Edition, Blackline Masters Master 2.4

Warm Up

Review with the class the meaning of a unit cost as the cost for one unit of the item. Also review estimation and reasonableness of answers.

Teaching Suggestions

Bring in some cans, bottles, etc., that show the amount they hold and their cost. Have the students estimate the unit cost by doing one-digit estimation. Bring in containers of identical items of different sizes and their prices, such as cereal boxes or cans of soup. For each item, compare the overall cost for the package and the unit cost. Discuss how the unit cost is usually, but not always, displayed at grocery stores. Have the students come up with the advantages and disadvantages of buying different sizes of the same product.

As a homework assignment, have the students find the unit cost of three items in their household. For each item, have them name the item, give its size and price, estimate the unit cost, and finally calculate the unit cost.

Assessment

Distribute *Assessment Master 7, A1.6A Estimate the Unit Cost: Quiz*, and have the students complete it. Collect and mark for formative assessment.

Specific Expectations

RE3.03, AG2.02, AG2.03, NA1.03

Overall Goals and Key Concepts

- connect steepness to rates of change
- relate rates of change to graphs
- introduce slope

Materials

- 4 or more sets of circular objects that are exactly the same, with at least 6 in each set (for example, CD's, buttons, pennies, margarine lids, washers, large coffee can lids, canning lids, poker chips)

Timing

100 min

Related Resources

MATHPOWER™ 9, Ontario Edition, Blackline Masters Master 1.1

1.6B Rates of Change

Student Resource pp. 60–61

Warm Up

Discuss with the class how the steepness of lines is related to rates of change. Introduce the term **slope**. Review Section 1.1.

Teaching Suggestions

Gather four or more sets of circular objects that are measurably different in size. Ensure that the objects in each set are exactly the same and that there are at least six of them. Supply each of your four stations with a full set of one object and a measuring tape. Or you can circulate the sets among your groups. Have the students fill in the hypothesis and gather data by circulating from station to station or by observing the sets as they are circulated. After they have completed the charts and graph, have the groups discuss questions 4 and 5 on student resource page 61. Have volunteers put their data on large chart paper. Encourage the students to choose the scale carefully for ease of discussion to follow. Discuss the answers with the class. Use a class graph to compare lines, and to discuss steepness and how it relates to each object. Tell the students that they will be revisiting this idea in the next unit, when they do slope. Relate this to unit costs calculated from Activity 1.6A.

Materials

- *Assessment Masters 8 to 11*
- *Teacher Resource Master 5* (Experiment Sheet)

Timing

225 min, spread over 2–3 days

Final Assessment

Teaching Suggestions

Send a letter home to be signed and returned, with details of dates and manner of assessment, several days prior to starting. Include the fact that the students will be given some work each night to prepare and help them understand the "words" in the assessment. Send home the first page of the half-life/pendulum swing experiments master the night before students are to do them in class. They can get help with reading and interpreting the questions at home. This will make the assessment go more smoothly. It is possible to do data collection for the pendulum swing or half-life experiments during the written test.

In part D of the Half-Life of Radioactive Substance Master, on teacher resource page 30, the blank in question 3 should be completed with a value that is a multiple of each student's answer to question 2.

For the Pendulum Swing Activity on teacher resource page 32, set up a pendulum and distribute *Teacher Resource Master 10* to each student in the class. Then, the students can "plug in" their graphing calculators to produce a graph.

A1.1C Rubric for Survey: Assignment

Category	LEVEL 1	LEVEL 2	LEVEL 3	LEVEL 4
Thinking and Inquiry – the survey question and the analysis of the results	– does not include a reasonable question with three answers for survey – requires much assistance to analyse results – does not understand assignment	– includes a reasonable question with two or three answers for survey – requires some assistance to analyse results – shows some understanding of assignment	– includes a good question with three answers for survey – requires little assistance to analyse results – shows good understanding of assignment	– excellent question with insightful answers for survey analysis of results – shows insight and clear understanding of assignment and purpose of survey
Knowledge and Understanding of Calculations – use the ratios or percents	– extension of survey results to all grade 9 students incorrect or not done (0) – finds only some results, but incorrect	– completes solution – some extensions of survey results to all grade 9 students correct	– solution complete – most extensions of survey results to all grade 9 students correct	– solution complete – all extensions of survey results to all grade 9 students correct, with appropriate extension
Applications – connects survey to all grade 9 students – discusses results	– does not understand connection – does not discuss, has limited understanding	– some understanding of connection – discusses with some understanding	– good understanding of connection – discusses with good understanding	– insightful understanding – discussed with excellent understanding
Communication Presentation – graph	– none, 1, or 2 of: • graph well scaled • used colour • used ruler • correct graph • titled	– incorrect graph but three or more of, or correct graph and two of: • graph properly scaled • good use of colour • used ruler • titled	– correct graph and three of: • graph properly scaled • good use of colour • used ruler • titled	– correct graph and all of: • graph properly scaled • excellent use of colour • used ruler • titled

A1.1C Survey: Quiz

A survey was conducted of 25 grade 9 students who were standing in the cafeteria. The question asked was

"What is your favourite fruit?"

The following questions refer to the survey above.
Full solutions are required for each question.

1. Who might be interested in the results of this survey?
    Explain.

2. The survey results are given in the table.

Which is Your Favourite Fruit?		
Fruit	**Tally**	**Total** (Complete this column.)
Bananas	⊤HL //	
Apples	⊤HL ⊤HL ⊤HL	
Oranges	///	

3. What percent of the students surveyed preferred bananas?

4. If there are 300 grade 9 students in your school, how many of them do you think will prefer apples? Explain your answer.

5. Make a bar graph or a circle graph of the results of this survey.

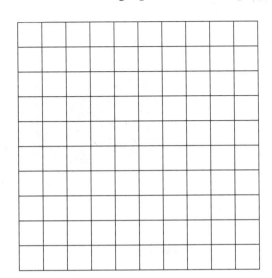 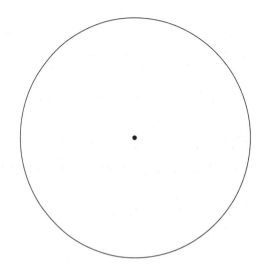

6. Do you think the survey was biased in any way? Explain.

7. How could the survey have been improved?

8. Use a graphing calculator to display these data on a bar graph. Show your graph to your teacher for evaluation before you clear it. (You may use your TI calculator instruction sheet for this.)

Name _____   Date _____

A1.2D Line of Best Fit: Quiz

Problem

Fourteen hikers were surveyed at Algonquin Park and asked,

"For how many days have you been hiking and how far did you travel in that time?"

The collected data are listed in the table below.

Number of Days Hiked	Distance Travelled (km)
1	12
1	12
2	18
3	19
3	21
5	23
5	25
6	23
7	30
7	31
9	37
10	39
11	41
12	52

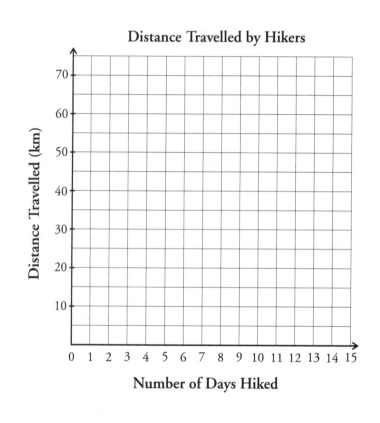

1. Use the grid provided to make a scatter plot of the information.

2. **a)** Draw the line of best fit.
   b) Explain how you decided where to draw your line.

3. Describe the relationship between the number of days hiked and the distance travelled, in kilometres.

4. Use your graph to predict each of the following.
   a) the distance, in kilometres, you would expect a hiker to travel in 4 days

   b) the number of days a hiker would need to travel 35 km

5. Who might be interested in these data and why?

A1.3E Two-Variable Relationships and Lines of Best Fit: Quiz

Problem 1

Time	Temperature (°C)
7:00 a.m.	12°
8:30 a.m.	15°
9:00 a.m.	16°
10:00 a.m.	19.5°
12:00 noon	24°
1:30 p.m.	30°
2:00 p.m.	35°

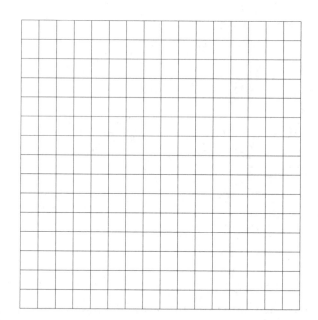

Part A

For the given data, make a hypothesis for the relationship. Include the answers to all five questions for a good hypothesis.

☞

☞

☞

☞

☞

Part B

Make a scatter plot. Join the points, using a line, or curve, of best fit, as appropriate.

Part C

Check your hypothesis and restate each item in your conclusions (report), making corrections if necessary.

Problem 2: Candle Length

Hours Lit	Candle Length (cm)
0	30
0.5	26
1.0	22
1.5	18
2.0	14
2.5	10
3.0	6

Part A
For the given data, make a hypothesis for the relationship. Include the answers to all five questions for a good hypothesis.

☞

☞

☞

☞

☞

Part B
Make a scatter plot and join the points, using a line, or curve of best fit, as appropriate. Label the axes and the graph appropriately.

Part C
Check your hypothesis and restate each item in your conclusions (report), making corrections if necessary.

A1.4C First Differences: Quiz

Part A

It is a hot summer day and Roma is filling the wading pool with water. She places the hose in the pool and notices the height of the water each minute as shown in the table below. Fill in the first-difference column.

Time (minutes)	Height (cm)	First Difference
1	3	
2	6	
3	9	
4	12	
5	15	
6	18	
7	21	

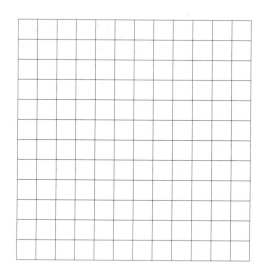

1. Describe what the first differences tell you about the relationship.

2. a) Make a scatter plot and draw the line of best fit.
   b) Does this graph support your answer to question 1? _____ Explain.

3. How long does it take for water in the wading pool to be

   a) 7 cm deep? _____   **b)** 30 cm deep? _____

4. Did you use interpolation or extrapolation for

   a) question 3 a)? _____

   b) question 3 b)? _____

Part B
Some molds grow according to the data shown in the chart below.
Fill out the first difference column.

Time (days)	Amount (g)	First Difference
1	40	
2	80	
3	160	
4	320	
5	640	

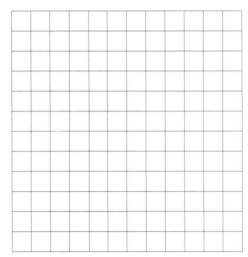

1. Describe what the first differences tell you about the relationship.

2. a) Make a scatter plot and draw the line/curve of best fit.

   b) Does this graph support your answer to question 1? _____
   Explain.

3. How long did it take to grow 100 g of mold? _____

4. When will there be 1000 g of mold? _____

Part C

Do the following sets of data describe a linear or non-linear relationship? Explain.

1.

x	y	First Difference
2	−5	
4	−10	
6	−15	
8	−20	
14	−25	
16	−35	
17	−40	

Linear or non-linear? Explain.

2.

x	y	First Difference
5	6	
4	4.5	
3	3	
2	1.5	
1	0	

Linear or non-linear? Explain.

3.

x	y	First Difference
5	100	
10	200	
15	400	
20	800	
25	1600	

Linear or non-linear? Explain.

A1.5E Story Time and Take a Walk: Quiz

1. The graph describes a person walking toward a wall.
   Tell the story which describes this graph.

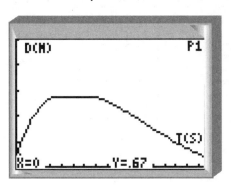

   Story

2. Draw a graph that describes each story:
   a) Alonso starts 0.5 m from a wall. He runs backward from the wall for 5 s.
   He then *slowly* walks to his starting position.

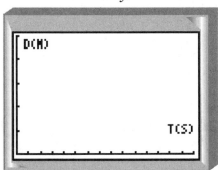

   b) Sarah starts at a point 6 m from a wall. She walks toward the wall for 3 s,
   stops for 3 s, then runs the rest of the way toward the wall.

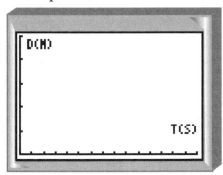

A1.6A Estimate the Unit Cost: Quiz

1. You can buy potatoes in small, medium, and large bags. Find the unit cost for each.

	Small 2 kg for $0.89	Medium 5 kg for $1.79	Large 10 kg for $3.49
Estimate.			
Is my answer reasonable?	Yes/No	Yes/No	Yes/No
Calculate the unit price.			

a) Which is the best buy?

b) If you were living with a friend, what size would you buy? Why?

2. Sports Club A offers 50 h of use of its facilities for $525.
   Sports Club B offers 40 h of use of its facilities for $475.

	Sport Club A	Sport Club B
Estimate. (Cost per hour)		
Is my answer reasonable?	Yes/No	Yes/No
Calculate the unit price. (Cost per hour)		

a) Which club offers the better deal?

b) Besides the cost, what else might you consider when joining a sports club?

How to Administer
the Unit 1 Summative Assessment

1. The assessment could be spread over four days.
   – mass experiment, day 1
   – half-life experiment, day 2
   – pendulum experiment, day 3
   – Relations and Graphing test, day 4

2. The pendulum swing can be done along with the Relations and Graphing test.

3. Groups of students can collect data for the half-life and the mass experiments. They can return to their seats and finish the paper work independently.

4. Each day, after the assessment, the students can be doing review to help with the next day's portion of the assessment.

5. The day before, the students can be provided with the first page of each of the first three activities from the assessment. In this way they will have time to process the language sufficiently. This is particularly true for the half-life experiment.

6. The pendulum swing works well if a small gift bag with a weight is hung from the ceiling with a heavy string. Clamp the motion detector at the correct height so that the students only need to plug in their calculator and "swing." Check the health and safety rules of the school.

7. When doing the half-life experiment, roll the dice into the lid of a cardboard box. This will be quieter and the dice will not scatter all over. The experiment may go more smoothly if you have some senior students to assist with the organization.

8. Be available to do questions orally with the students, particularly those with learning disabilities. Be willing to read, write, and interpret the questions.

"Being willing to read and write to an L.D. student is like allowing a student with visual impairment to wear glasses."

T. Anne and Rod Yeager

Unit 1 Final Assessment: Part 1
Mass vs. Number of Items

Experiment: You will need 8 identical items, a pail, and a scale from which to hang the pail. Gather data by placing the items, one by one, into the pail and reading the mass from the scale. Complete questions 1–5 using *Teacher Resource Master 2* (Experiment Sheet) provided by your teacher.

1. Make a good hypothesis.
2. Gather the data.
3. Fill in the first differences column.
4. Make the scatter plot and draw the line of best fit.
5. Make a conclusion. Your conclusion should include all items from your hypothesis, with any corrections needed.

After completing the above, answer the following questions.

1. Who might be interested in this data and why?

2. Study your graph. Estimate the mass of 5.5 items.

   _____

3. Study your graph. Estimate how many items have a total mass of 5 kg.

   _____

4. Study your graph. Estimate the mass of 14 items. _____

5. Estimate the mass of 2000 items. _____

   Describe how you got your answer.

Final Assessment: Part 2
Half-Life of Radioactive Substance

Radioactive decay is the term used to describe the breakdown of the atoms of a radioactive substance. The **rate of decay** depends upon the substance. The time it takes for a substance to decay to half the original amount is known as the **half-life** of the substance.

Example

The half-life of iodine is 15 minutes. If you begin with 4000 atoms of iodine, this means that 2000 atoms will remain after 15 minutes, _____ atoms will remain after the next 15 minutes or after a total of 30 minutes, and 500 atoms will remain after the next _____ minutes or after a total of _____ minutes.

The following experiment will demonstrate the decay of a different radioactive substance. About $\frac{1}{6}$ of the atoms will decay each hour. This experiment will determine how long it takes for this substance to decay to half of the original amount.

Part A: Hypothesis

Use the descriptors discussed in this unit (linear/non-linear, positive/negative, (0, 0), continuous/discrete) to write a hypothesis describing the relationship between the number of atoms remaining and the time in hours.

☞

☞

☞

☞

☞

Part B: Data Collection
Follow the directions and complete the chart below.

1. You will be given a container of 100 dice. Each die represents 1 atom of a radioactive substance. Thus, the contents of your container represent 100 atoms.

2. **Process**
   Each pour of the dice represents one hour. Dice with 1 showing on top represent the atoms that have decayed during the hour.
   Step 1   Pour the dice (atoms), *A*, onto a tray.
               Remove the dice (atoms) showing 1. These are the atoms that have decayed.
   Step 2   Count the number of dice (atoms) remaining.
   Step 3   Record the data in the chart.
   Step 4   Replace the remaining dice (atoms) in the container.

3. Repeat steps 1 to 4 of the process to determine the number of atoms that remain after 2 h, then again after 3 h, and so on, until fewer than 5 dice (atoms) remain.

Number of Hours	Number of Atoms Remaining	Number of Hours	Number of Atoms Remaining
0	100		
1			
2			

Part C

1. Construct a graph of the time in hours vs. the number of atoms remaining.

2. Use your graph to revise your hypothesis from Part A.
   Be specific about the differences.

Part D:

Answer each of the following questions in the space provided.

1. **a)** Study your data and graph. Estimate how many hours it took for 100 atoms to reduce to 50 atoms.

    _____ h

    b) How many hours did it take for 50 atoms to reduce to 25 atoms?

    _____ h

2. Consider your answers in question 1 above. Predict the half-life of this substance. Explain your reasoning.

3. Use your results from question 2. Suppose you start with 500 atoms of this substance. How many atoms will remain after _____ hours? (*Raise your hand to have this blank filled in by your teacher.*)

    Explain how you got your answer.

4. Will this substance ever decay to zero atoms? Explain.

5. **Bonus:** Write an equation that represents the relationship between the atoms remaining (R) and the amount of time (t), in hours, that has passed.

    _____

Part E:

1. Suppose a substance decays at a constant rate of 10 atoms per hour. (In other words, 10 atoms decay each hour.) There are 100 atoms at the start. Complete the following chart.

Number of Hours	Number of Atoms Remaining
0	100
1	

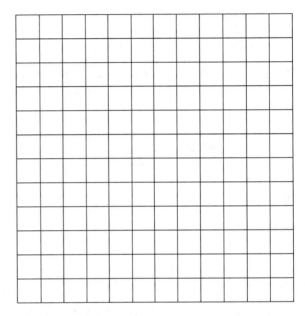

2. Use the grid to construct the graph of the time in hours vs. the number of atoms remaining.

3. Describe the similarities and differences between this graph and the graph you made with the dice in Part C. Use appropriate mathematical language.

4. Form an equation that represents the relationship between the number of atoms remaining, R, and the time, t, in hours, that has passed.

Final Assessment: Part 3
Pendulum Swing Activity

Part A
Your teacher will demonstrate a pendulum swinging in the doorway of your classroom. Draw a graph of time vs. distance that the pendulum is away from the teacher. (You may need to estimate time and distance.) Use a horizontal scale of 1 to 15 s and a vertical scale of 1 to 5 m. Hand in your graph to your teacher.

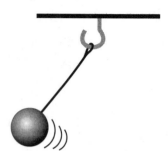

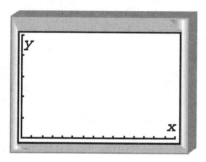

Your teacher will call upon you to do Part B. You may bring your technology sheet with you, because you will be using the motion detectors (CBR™) to check your answer above.

Part B
Set up the CBR™ and the graphing calculator to use the **Ranger** program.

Arrange the CBR™ to read the motion of the pendulum from where your teacher was standing.

When you are satisfied with your results, carefully copy the graph from your calculator to this sheet, being mindful of distances and times.

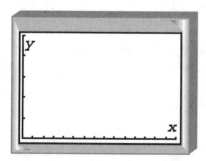

Part C

1. Compare Graphs A and B that you produced in Parts A and B.

   a) In what ways are the graphs the same? (Be specific.)

   b) In what ways are the graphs different? (Be specific.)

   c) Why do you think each difference occurred?

2. a) Describe in words, or draw a graph, to show how the graph would differ if the pendulum started away from the motion detector instead of close to it.

   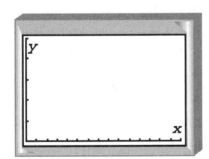

   b) Use Graph B to estimate the amount of time it takes for the pendulum to do one full swing. (A full swing is all the way to one side, then, all the way to the other side, and, then, back to the starting position.)

3. Use graph B to answer these questions. (Be as exact as possible.)
   a) How *close* did the pendulum get to the motion detector

      (i) during the first 3 s? _____

      (ii) during the last 3 s? _____

   b) How far did the pendulum go from the motion detector

      (i) during the first 3 s? _____

      (ii) during the last 3 s? _____

4. Explain why the distances differ from the beginning to the end of the time?

5. If you could have recorded the swinging pendulum until 5 s after the swinging
   had stopped, show what you think the graph would look like.

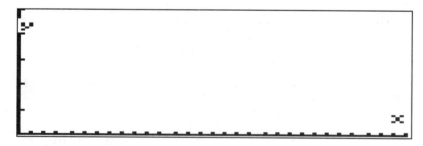

Final Assessment: Part 4
Relations and Graphing

1. Joe is interested in knowing the favourite fruit juice of the 220 grade 9 students at his school. He uses his math class as a sample. He asks this question:

   "Do you prefer orange juice or another juice?"

   a) Has Joe created bias in the wording of the question? If you answer yes, write a new question that is without bias. If you answer no, explain why.

   b) The results of his class survey are displayed in the chart below:

Flavour	Number of Students
Orange	11
Grape	8
Peach	4

   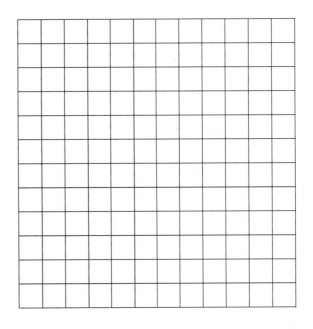

   Display the data on the grid provided or on a graphing calculator. If you use the calculator, show your results to your teacher for marking.

   c) What percent of the students in the class prefer grape juice? (Show your work.)

d) Of the 220 grade 9 students in the school, how many prefer orange juice?

2. Estimate, then calculate, the **unit cost** of a pack of peach juice if a 24-pack of peach juice costs $7.98. (Show your work.)

Estimation:

Calculation:

3. The scatter plot shows the number of fruit flies living after they have been sprayed.

   a) Draw the line of best fit.

   b) Describe the relationship between the number of fruit flies and the number of hours since spraying.

   c) Interpolate from your line of best fit how long after spraying there are 100 fruit flies left.

   d) Interpolate from your line of best fit how many fruit flies are alive 2.5 h after spraying.

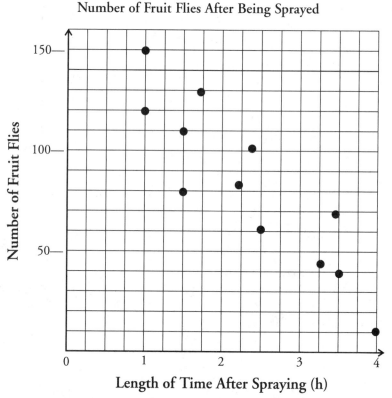

Number of Fruit Flies After Being Sprayed

4. For each of the following, make up your own example of the type of correlation, draw the graph needed, and label the axes.

    a) positive correlation   **b)** negative correlation   **c)** no correlation

5. How does finding first differences help determine whether a relationship is linear or non-linear?

6. a) Calculate the first differences. Show your work.
    b) Are the data linear or non-linear? Explain.

Month	Average Temperature (°C)	First Differences
January	−4	
February	−1	
March	2	
April	5	
May	8	

    c) What is the average rate of change of temperature per month?

7. **a)** The graph shows one of Nicola's trips from her home to the video store. Write a story describing her trip. Refer to speeds, distances, and times in your story.

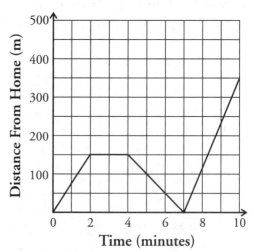

Nicola's Trip From Home to the Video Store

b) How far is Nicola's home from the video store?

8. Grapefruit is being packed into heavy wooden boxes. The graph at the right shows the relationship of the mass of the box and its contents vs. the number of grapefruit, as the grapefruit are packed one by one into the wooden box.

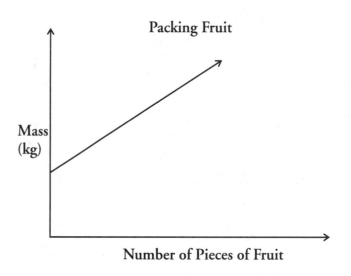

Packing Fruit

a) Explain why the graph does not start at (0, 0).

b) Use a dotted line to show the relationship of the mass of the box and its contents vs. the number of grapefruit in the box, if a light plastic box is used instead of a wooden box. A scale is not necessary.

c) With a different colour, draw a line on the given graph to show how the graph would look if lemons were being packed into the wooden box instead of grapefruit.

Student Resource Answers

Unit 1 Relationships in Mathematics

1.1 Data Collection and Analysis

1.1B Using Surveys to Gather Data   pp. 3–5

1. Answers may vary. No, not all grade 9 students have an equal chance of being in the sample.
2., 3., 4. Answers will vary.
5. Answers may vary.
   a) The sample is not representative of the whole grade 9 population so reliability is probably low;
   b) The sample is not representative of the whole grade 9 population so it may be biased.
   c) Yes, the question has been answered.
   d) Take a random sample from the whole grade 9 population to get better results.

1.1C Survey Assignment   pp. 6–7

All answers will vary.

1.1 D Learning Styles Inventory: pp. 8–10

Personal Results
All answers will vary.

1.1 E Learning Styles Inventory: pp. 11–13

Class Results
All answers will vary.

1.1F Drawing a Histogram or Bar   pp. 14–15

Graph on the TI–83 Plus
Answers will vary.

1.2 Scatter Plots to Show Relationships

1.2A What Is a Scatter Plot?   pp. 16–19

Example

1.
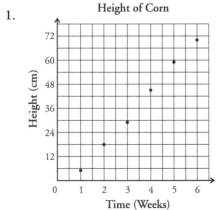
Height of Corn

2. Yes, the growth of corn is continuous.
3. increases
4. Yes, the corn would not be growing, and it might not be ready for the farmer to sell.

Practice

1. a)

Number of Litres	Cost of This Gas

   b) Horizontal axis - Number of Litres
      Vertical axis - Cost of Gas
   c) (4, $0.15)
   d) The graph would be a straight line starting at (0, 0).
   e) Yes, you may pump part of a litre of gas.

2. a)
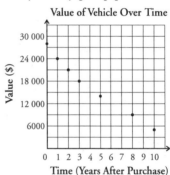
Value of Vehicle Over Time

   b) increases; decreases
   c) continuous; the value of the vehicle decreases throughout each year.
   d) Answers may vary: damage, rust, number of kilometres

3. a)
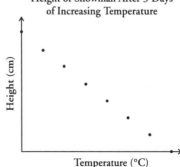
Height of Snowman After 3 Days of Increasing Temperature

   b) As the temperature increases, the height of the snowman decreases, because the snowman melts.

1.2 B Positive, Negative, or No Correlation?

pp. 20–23

Example 1

a)

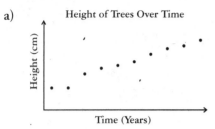

Height of Trees Over Time

b) positive correlation c) increases

Example 2

a)

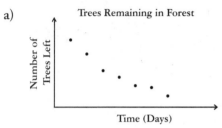

Trees Remaining in Forest

b) negative correlation c) decreases

Example 3

a)

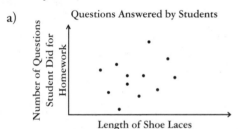

Questions Answered by Students

b) no correlation c) varies

Student Created Examples

Answers may vary. For example,

a) positive correlation

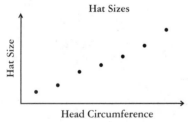

Hat Sizes

This is a positive correlation because, as head size increases, hat size also increases.

b) negative correlation

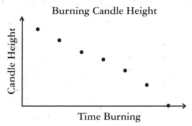

Burning Candle Height

This is a negative correlation because, as time of burning increases, the candle height decreases.

c) no correlation

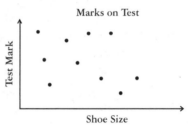

Marks on Test

There is no correlation, because there is no relationship or pattern between shoe size and test marks.

Practice

1. a) neither; There is no pattern in the scatter plot.
    b) positive; As the independent variable increases, the dependant variable also increases.
    c) negative; As the independent variable increases, the dependent variable decreases.
    d) positive; As the independent variable increases, the dependent variable also increases.

2. a) negative; The number of pages left to be typed decreases as the number of pages typed increases.
    b) no; There is no relationship or pattern between the size of a student's hand and the number of rings he or she owns.
    c) positive; The number of people swimming increases as the temperature outside increases.
    d) positive; The depth of Lake Ontario increases as the amount of rainfall and snow that year increases.
    e) negative; The number of centimetres of ice on Island Lake decreases as the outside winter temperature increases.
    f) positive; Your math mark increases as the number of hours you study increases.
    g) positive; Your take-home pay increases as the number of hours you work increases.
    h) negative; The energy left in your radio decreases as the number of hours you have listened to it increases.

1.2C Drawing the Line of Best Fit   pp. 24–25

1.
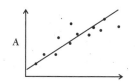

2. Answers may vary. Draw a line that is close to as many points as possible.
3. a) positive   b) negative
4. Answers may vary. For example,
   a) A person's height increases as his or her age increases.
   b) A person's appetite decreases as the amount of food he or she eats increases.
6. Answers may vary.
   a)
   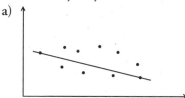

   b) Yes; The correlation between these points is not strong. It is difficult to draw a line through more than two points.
7. Answers may vary.

1.2D Practice: Scatter Plots and Lines of Best Fit   pp. 26–28

1. a)
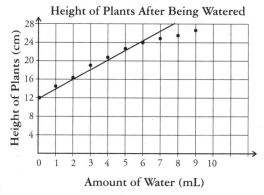

   b) The height of plants increases as the amount of water increases.
2. 8.5 cm
3. 19 cm
4. Answers may vary. Line of best fit may vary from your partner's slightly.

5. a), b)
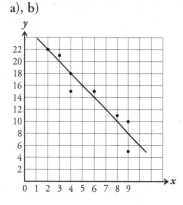

6. a) positive; As the number of hours increases so will the number of boxes of nails used.
   b), c)
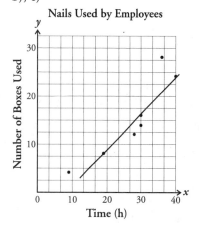

   Yes. In general, as the time increases, the number of boxes of nails used increases.
   d) 10   e) 42

1.2E Describing Relationships   pp. 29–30

a)
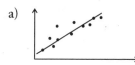

no relationship; positive correlation; linear

b)

relationship; negative correlation; linear

c)

no relationship; no correlation; non-linear

d)

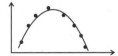

relationship; positive correlation, then negative correlation; non-linear

e)

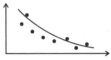

relationship; negative correlation; linear

1.3 Finding Relationships

1.3A The Hypothesis and the Conclusion   p. 31

Answers may vary.

1.3B Cooling Temperature vs. Time   p. 32

Answers may vary.

1.3C Can You Find a Relationship?   pp. 33–37

Answers may vary.

1.3D Investigation: Finding Relationships   p. 38

Answers may vary.

1.3E Make an Experiment of Your Own   pp. 39–40

Answers may vary.

1.3F Summary Page and Journal   p. 41

Answers may vary.

1. scatter plot - a graph of data that are a series of points
2. line of best fit - a line that passes as close as possible to a set of plotted points
3. linear relation - a relation that can be represented by a straight-line graph
   non-linear relation - a relation that cannot be represented by a straight-line graph
4. positive correlation - a relation in which, when one variable increases, the other variable increases
   negative correlation - a relation in which, when one variable increases, the other variable decreases
   no correlation - no pattern or clear relationship between data
5. discrete data - data for which you cannot connect the points on a scatter plot
   continuous data - data for which you can connect the points on a scatter plot

6.
   - Does the relationship have a positive, a negative, or no correlation?
   - What is an explanation of the relationship?
   - Is the relationship non-linear?
   - Is the origin, (0, 0), a reasonable element of the set of data?
   - Is the relationship discrete or continuous?

1.4 Is It Really Linear?

1.4A Expressions Involving Integers   pp. 42–44

1.

x	6	2	0	–3	–5	–10
4	24	8	0	–12	–20	–40
1	6	2	0	–3	–5	–10
0	0	0	0	0	0	0
–1	–6	–2	0	3	5	10
–3	–18	–6	0	9	15	30

Conclusions

positive; positive; negative

Practice

1. a) 21   b) –8   c) 15   d) –7
   e) 2   f) –3   g) –2   h) 10
2. a) 9   b) –8

Practice

1. a) –1   b) 3   c) –7
   d) 7   e) –8   f) –12

Practice

1. a) –2   b) 5   c) –9   d) –9
   e) 9   f) –6   g) 8   h) 2

1.4B Relationships and First Differences   p. 45

linear
Data
First differences are all 1.50.

1.

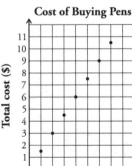

Cost of Buying Pens

2. Yes.
3. equal; linear

1.4C Practice: First Differences

pp. 46–48

First Set of Data
First differences are all 6.

Second Set of Data
First differences are all –20.

In the first case, the independent variable, x, increases by the same amount (1), and the dependent variable, y, increases by the same amount (6).

Conclusion: The relationship is linear and has a negative correlation.

Third Set of Data
First differences are 10, 20, 30, 40, and 50.

In each case, the independent variable, x, increases by the same amount (+4), and the dependent variable, y, increases by different amounts.

Conclusion: The relationship is non-linear and has a positive correlation.

Fourth Set of Data
First differences are all 40.

In each case, when the independent variable increases by the same amount (+2), the dependent variable increases by the same amount (+40). When the independent variable increases by +4, the dependent variable increases by +80. Proportionally, these are equal. Thus, the relationship is linear and has a positive correlation.

Fifth Set of Data
All first differences are 0.5

In each case, when the independent variable increases by the same amount (+10), the dependent variable increases by the same amount (+0.5). When the independent variable increases by +20, the dependent variable increases by +1.0. Proportionally, these are equal. Thus, the relationship is linear and has a positive correlation.

Sixth Set of Data
First differences are –3.5, –7, 9, –11 and 13.

In each case, the independent variable, x, increases by the same amount (+1), and the dependent variable, y, increases by different amounts.

Conclusion: The relationship is non-linear, and there is no correlation.

1.5 Combination Relationships

1.5A More Relationships

pp. 49–50

Relationships can be linear. This means that a straight line can be drawn through the points.

Relationships can be non-linear. This means that a straight line cannot be drawn through the points.

Relationships can have a positive correlation. This means that when the independent variable increases, the dependent variable increases.

Relationships can have a negative correlation. This means that, when the independent variable increases, the dependent variable decreases.

Relationships can be a combination of the above. This means that a relationship can be linear and have a positive or negative correlation. A relationship can also be non-linear and have a positive or negative correlation.

1.
Leaves on a Maple Tree Throughout a Year

2.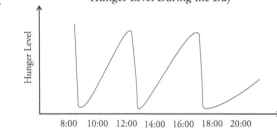
Hunger Level During the Day

3.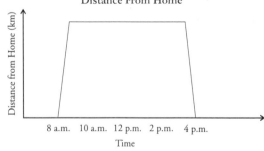
Distance From Home

4.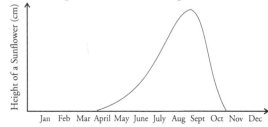
Height of Sunflower Throughout the Year

1.5B A Picture Goes With the Story
p. 51

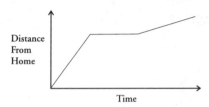

1.5C Graphs That Represent a Story
p. 52

1.

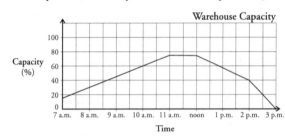

Answers may vary.

On Friday the vending machine contains 200 cans of pop at 8 a.m. No cans of pop are bought before 10 a.m. At recess, 80 cans of pop are bought between 10 a.m. and 11 a.m. No cans of pop are bought between 11 a.m. and 11:30 a.m. During lunch, between 11:30 a.m. and 1 p.m., 100 can of pop are bought. Between 1 p.m. and 1:45 p.m., no cans of pop are bought. Between 1:45 p.m. and 2 p.m., the machine id filled with cans of pop. Between 2 p.m. and 3 p.m., when classes are in sessions, no cans of pop are bought . School ends at 3 p.m., and there are 40 cans of pop bought before 3:30 p.m.

1.5E Take a Walk and Tell the Story
pp. 54–57

Part A

1.

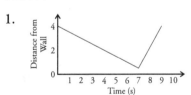

2.

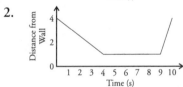

3.

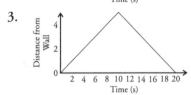

4.

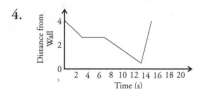

5.

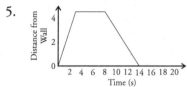

6.

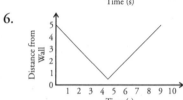

7.

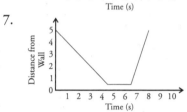

Part B

Answers may vary.

1. Facing the wall and beginning 2 m from the wall, I ran backward from the wall. When I was 4 m from the wall, I stopped for 2 s, then walked slowly backward from the wall for 1 m. Then, I stopped.

2. Beginning 5 m from the wall, I ran toward the wall. When I was 0.5 m from the wall, I walked backward to my starting position. Then, I stopped.

3. Beginning 5 m from the wall, I waited 3 s. I walked until I was 0.5 m from the wall. Then, I stopped.

4. Answers may vary. Beginning 5 m from the wall, I walked for 2 s. I waited 3 s and then walked backward to my starting position.

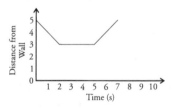

1.6 Rates of Change

1.6A Estimate and Calculate pp. 58–59

Unit Rates

1.

	Small 50 mL for $2.19	Medium 100 mL for $3.79	Large 200 mL for $5.49
Estimate.	$\frac{2}{50}$ = $0.04/mL	$\frac{4}{100}$ = $0.04/mL	$\frac{3}{150}$ = $0.025/mL
Is my answer reasonable?	Yes	Yes	Yes
Unit cost for each size	$0.044/mL	$0.038/mL	$0.027/mL

Large is the best buy.

2.

	Small 45 g for $1.29	Regular 80 g for $1.79	Large 150 g for $2.89
Estimate.	$\frac{1}{45}$ = $0.02/g	$\frac{2}{80}$ = $0.025/g	$\frac{3}{150}$ = $0.02/g
Is my answer reasonable?	Yes	Yes	Yes
Unit cost for each size	$0.029/g	$0.022/g	$0.019/g

Large is the best buy.
A person with a smaller appetite may find that the quantities are too large.

3.

	Sample 125 mL for $3.99	1 L for $12.19	4 L for $28.79
Estimate.	$\frac{4}{125}$ = $0.032/mL	$\frac{12}{200}$ = $0.06/mL	$\frac{29}{4000}$ = $0.007/mL
Is my answer reasonable?	Yes	Yes	Yes
Unit cost for each size.	$0.032/mL	$0.012/mL	$0.007/mL

4 L is the best buy.
A 4-L can may be too large for the surface to be painted.

4.

	CD Club A	CD Club B
Estimate.	$\frac{65}{13}$ = $5/CD	$\frac{55}{11}$ = $5/CD
Is my answer reasonable?	Yes	Yes
Unit cost for each CD.	$5/CD	$5/CD

Answers may vary: selection, how long you have to stay a member, how many more CDs must be purchased.

1.6B Rates of Change pp. 60–61

Possible answers

1.

Type of Disk: CD		
Number of Disks	Total Length (cm)	First Difference
1	12	
		12
2	24	
		12
3	36	
		12
4	48	
		12
5	60	

Type of Disk: Lid of a Jar		
Number of Disks	Total Length (cm)	First Difference
1	6	
		6
2	12	
		6
3	18	
		6
4	24	
		6
5	30	

Type of Disk: Loonie		
Number of Disks	Total Length (cm)	First Difference
1	2.5	
		2.5
2	5	
		2.5
3	7.5	
		2.5
4	10	
		2.5
5	12.5	

Type of Disk: Quarter		
Number of Disks	Total Length (cm)	First Difference
1	2.2	
		2.2
2	4.4	
		2.2
3	6.6	
		2.2
4	8.8	
		2.2
5	11.0	

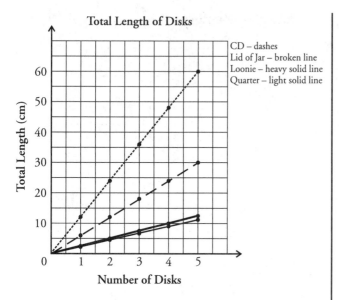

Total Length of Disks

CD – dashes
Lid of Jar – broken line
Loonie – heavy solid line
Quarter – light solid line

4. a) They are all straight lines.
   b) The steepness of the lines increases as the length of the disks increases.
5. a) The first differences are equal, and they are the same as the length of the disk.
   b) The first difference equals the slope of the line and the rate of change.

Teacher's Resource Answers

Unit 1 Relationships in Mathematics

A1.1C Survey: Quiz
pp. 15–16

1. the food service providers at the school
   It would help them decide how much of each of the three fruit varieties they should buy, so they could reduce waste and increase profits.
2. Totals: bananas: 7; apples: 15; oranges: 3
3. 28% preferred bananas.
4. 180 students would prefer apples.
5.

Favourite Fruit   Favourite Fruit

OR

6. Yes. The survey does not represent the whole grade 9 population since the survey sample is small. Students' choices are restricted to only three fruit varieties. It does not represent the students in other grades that would buy fruit in the cafeteria.
7. The survey could be improved by surveying a larger sample of students and providing more fruit choices.
8. on graphing calculator screen

A1.2D Line of Best Fit: Quiz
pp. 17–18

1., 2. a)

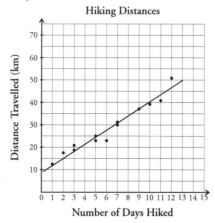

Hiking Distances

   b) The line of best fit follows the direction suggested by the plotted points.
3. There is a positive correlation between days hiked and distance travelled. The distance travelled increases as the number of days hiked increases.
4. a) 22 km   b) 9 days
5. Park personnel could use the data to determine the average daily hiking rate. This information would help them plan hiking routes and the locations of rest areas. Search and Rescue teams may extrapolate from the data to estimate distances travelled by lost hikers.

A1.3E Two Variable Relationships and Lines of Best Fit: Quiz
pp. 19–20

Problem 1

Part A: Answers may vary.

Part B:

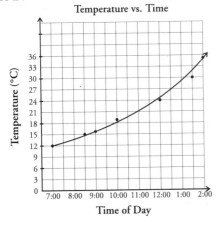

Temperature vs. Time

Part C: Answers will vary.

Problem 2

Parts A, B, and C: Answers will vary.

A1.4C First Differences: Quiz   pp. 21–23

Part A

All first differences = 3

1. In each case, when the time increases by 1 minute, the height increases by 3 cm. Thus, the relationship is linear and has a positive correlation.

2. a)

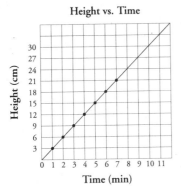

Height vs. Time

   b) Yes, the pattern in the plotted points is increasing and suggests a straight line. The relationship is linear.

3. a) 2.3 minutes   b) 10 minutes
4. a) interpolation   b) extrapolation

Part B

First differences: 40, 80, 160, 320

1. In each case, the time increases by the same amount (1) and the height increases by different positive amounts. Conclusion: The relationship is non-linear and has a positive correlation.

2. a)

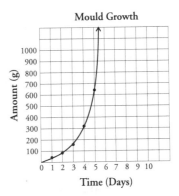

Mould Growth

   b) Yes, the pattern in the plotted points is increasing but it does not suggest a line. The relationship is non-linear.

3. 2.3 days
4. 5.6 days

Part C

1. All first differences = –5.
   Although the first differences are all equal, the independent variable does not increase by the same amount. Thus, the first differences do not increase by the same amount for the same increase in the independent variable. As the independent variable increases, the dependent variable decreases. Conclusion: The relationship is non-linear, and there is a negative correlation.

2. All first differences = –1.5.
   When the independent variable decreases by the same amount (+1), the dependent variable decreases by the same amount. Conclusion: The relationship is linear, and there is a positive correlation.

3. First differences: 100, 200, 400, 800
   When the independent variable increases by the same amount (+5), the dependent variable increases by different amounts. Conclusion: The relationship is non-linear, and there is a positive correlation.

A1.5E Story Time and Take a Walk: Quiz   p. 24

1. The person begins 0.67 m from the wall and walks about 2 m away from the wall in 3 s. The person waits here for 4 s, then, returns to the starting position at a slower pace about 8 s later.

2. a)

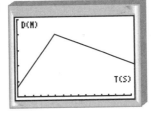

b)

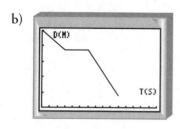

A1.6A Estimate the Unit Cost: Quiz

p. 25

1.

	Small 2 kg for $0.89	Medium 5 kg for $1.79	Large 10 kg for $3.49
Estimate.	$0.50	$0.40	$0.35
Is my answer reasonable?	Yes	Yes	Yes
Calculate the unit price.	$0.45	$0.36	$0.35

a) The large bag is the best buy.
b) Answers will vary, depending on eating preferences, eating habits, and storage facilities.

2.

	Sport Club A	Sport Club B
Estimate.	$10.00	$12.50
Is my answer reasonable?	Yes	Yes
Calculate the unit price.	$10.50	$11.88

a) Sport Club A is the better deal at $10.50/h.
b) Answers may vary. Some things to consider are hours of operation, location, and access to equipment.

Unit 1 Final Assessment Activity: Part 1

pp. 26–27

Mass vs. Number of Items

Experiment Sheet: Answers may vary.
1. The manufacturer of the rope holding the pail to the scale may be interested in knowing the breaking point of the rope. The manufacturer of the pail may want to know how many items can be stored in the pail for a given mass.
2., 3., 4., 5. Answers will vary.

Unit 1 Final Assessment Activity: Part 2

pp. 28–32

Half-Life of Radioactive Substance

Example: 1000 atoms will remain after the next 15 minutes, and 500 atoms after the next 15 minutes or after a total of 45 minutes.

Part A: Hypothesis

Answers may vary.

Part B: Data Collection

3. Theoretically, 0.83 of the atoms remain after each pour. Answers may vary.

Part C

1. Answers will vary. However, the graph should show a decreasing exponential relationship between number of atoms remaining and time.

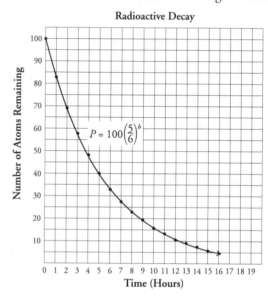

2. Answers may vary.

Part D

1. Answers may vary.
   a) About 3.8 h   b) About 3.8 h
2. The half-life is about 3.8 h, since half of the original amount remains after 3.8 h and half of the remaining (one quarter of the original) is present after another 3.8 h (7.6 h from the start).
3. Answers will depend on data provided by the teacher and may vary according to the half-life determined in question 2.
4. Yes, this substance will decay to zero atoms. After sufficient pours of the dice (time), there will be no atoms remaining. Based on the pattern in the experimental results, it is taking longer for the atoms to decay. Eventually there will be zero atoms remaining.
5. Answers may vary. For example, $R = 100(0.83)^t$, or $R = 100\left(\dfrac{5}{6}\right)^t$.

48 *Unit 1 Teacher's Resource Answers*

Copyright © 2002 McGraw-Hill Ryerson Limited

Part E

1. **Number of Hours:** 0, 1, 2, 3, 4, 5, 6, 7, 8
   Number of Atoms Remaining: 100, 90, 80, 70, 60, 50, 40, 30, 20

2.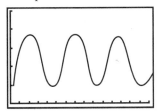

3. This graph forms a line. Thus it shows that the relationship between number of atoms remaining and time is linear. The graph in Part C forms a curve and is non-linear. There is a negative correlation between number of atoms remaining and time for both graphs.

4. $R = -10t + 100$

Unit 1 Final Assessment: Part 3

pp. 33–35

Part A

One possible solution for a pendulum:

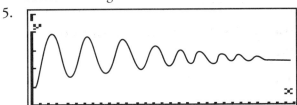

Part B

Answers will vary depending on data collection techniques and skill.

Part C

1. a) Answers will vary, depending on the results in Part A. Both graphs are non-linear. Both show that the pendulum is moving closer and farther away from the position of the motion detector. The motion is periodic, and the distance travelled by the pendulum on each swing is decreasing.

   b) Answers will vary in terms of height along the vertical axis (amplitude of swing) and number of cycles recorded (period of oscillation) along the horizontal axis. The starting position of the pendulum relative to

the motion detector will determine the position of the graph along the vertical axis.

   c) Answers may vary. For example, the larger the amplitude of the swing, the higher up the vertical axes the graph will rise. If the pendulum is given an initial velocity, it will complete more cycles during data collection. Poor data collection techniques, such as interference within the detection zone and irregular swing patterns, will give unexpected results.

2. a) If the pendulum starts away from the motion detector, the graph would begin higher up on the vertical axis, fall towards the horizontal axis, and rise upwards. This motion repeats in the same manner as the original graph. The distance travelled during each swing would decrease as well.

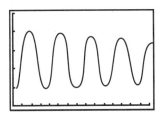

   b) Answers may vary.

3. Answers may vary.

4. The distances differ, because air resistance reduces the amplitude of the pendulum swing. Each successive swing travels a shorter distance.

5.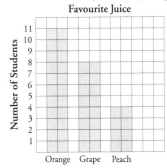

Unit 1 Final Assessment: Part 4

pp. 36–39

Relations and Graphing

1. a) Yes; he has created a bias, since not all juices are equally represented. A better question is, "What kind of juice do you prefer?"

   b)

   Favourite Juice

c) 34.8% preferred grape juice.

d) 105 students would prefer orange juice.

2. $0.33

3. **a)**

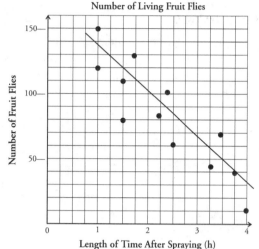

Number of Living Fruit Flies

b) There is a negative correlation between the number of fruit flies left and the number of hours after spraying. As the number of hours after spraying increases, the number of fruit flies left decreases.

c) 2 hours after spraying

d) 85 fruit flies are left

4. **a)** positive correlation

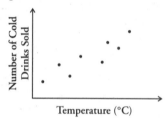

b) negative correlation

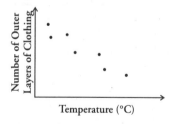

c) no correlation

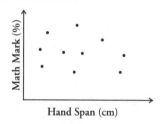

5. If the first differences are the same number and the independent variable changes by equal increments then you can state that the relationship is linear. If one or more of these conditions is not met, the relationship is non-linear.

6. **a)** All first differences = 3.

b) The data are linear. For each month that passes, there is a 3°C increase in the average temperature.

c) The average rate of change of temperature is 3°C/month.

7. **a)** Answers may vary. One story idea is: Nicola was about to leave for a party when her parents asked her to pick up a "new release" video that had just been returned to the video store. Nicola needed to get there before anyone else checked out the video, so she ran to the video store, 150 m away, at the rate of 75 m/min. It took 2 minutes to find the video and check it out. She was weary from her run to the store, so she walked back to her house at the rate of 50 m/min. She handed the video to her parents, who were waiting at the door of her house, and immediately headed to the party. Nicola was 7 minutes behind schedule. She was anxious to get there, so she ran the entire 350 m in 3 minutes. Her average speed during this time was 116.7 m/min.

b) Nicola's house is 150 m from the video store.

8. **a)** The graph does not start at (0, 0) because the empty box itself has mass.

b), c)

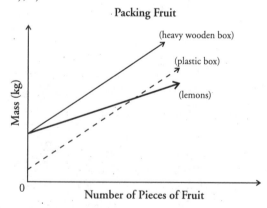

Packing Fruit

Unit 2 Teaching Notes

Section 2.1 Exponents

The first three activities of this section deal with algebraic concepts and skills, many of which are drill in nature. Students find these activities difficult. Rather than frustrating yourself and the students, review them frequently throughout the unit with mini practice opportunities. Applications are also needed. It is possible to introduce a second topic simultaneously. Suggestions include:

- slopes of ramps and stairs, Sections 2.4, 2.5, and 2.6 of the student resource
- area and perimeter, Sections 3.1 and 3.2 of the student resource
- *The Geometer's Sketchpad®*, Section 3.6 of the student resource.

2.1A Exponents: Introduction

Student Resource pp. 66–68

Teaching Suggestions

Display student resource page 66 on an overhead projector so that the students can fill out their own sheets correctly as you go. Provide each student with a sheet of paper to fold. Complete as a class Exercises 1 to 3 on student resource page 66. Count the sections with them the first few times. Discuss how the number of sections doubles after each fold. When the students describe the relationship, it may be necessary to graph it first. Use the same scale for both activities (i.e., doubling and tripling). Use the graphs as an aid in discussing the topics linear/non-linear, positive/negative, and appropriateness of (0, 0). Speculate with the students on the thickness of the paper after it is folded in half 50 times. The students are often astounded to find that the answer is over 100 000 000 km.

Repeat the activity for tripling, that is, folding the paper in thirds. Have students try this on their own or in pairs. If the graphs are on overheads, the two graphs can be overlaid and students can see how much faster one grows than the other. At this point, define the meaning of **exponent**. Complete with the class Example 1 on student resource page 68 and, then, have the students complete Example 2 on student resource page 68 on their own.

Have scientific calculators available, and show them how to use the exponent button.

Common Errors

This may be the first time the students have seen exponential notation on a calculator. Ensure that they understand how to reformat a number given in scientific notation on a calculator screen into the format given on the student resource page.

> "When teaching something new, say it, show it, and let the students do it."
>
> T. Anne and Rod Yeager

Specific Expectations
NA 2.01, NA2.05

Overall Goals and Key Concepts
- understand how things can grow exponentially, not linearly

Materials
- overhead projector
- sheets of paper

Timing
75 min

2.1B Understanding Powers: Exponent Rules

Student Resource pp. 69–72

Teaching Suggestions
Encourage the students to understand the rules, not just memorize them. Students may continue to struggle with integers. This section provides more opportunity for practice of this important skill.

Common Errors
Stress that, when applying the rules of exponents, the bases must always be the same and that the base remains the same throughout. Explain that the rules do not change, even if there is a negative sign in the base or in the exponent.

Assessment
Distribute *Assessment Master 12*, A2.1B Exponents: Quiz, and have the students complete it. Collect and mark for formative assessment.

"At least 50 percent of a teacher's job is encouragement."

T. Anne and Rod Yeager

2.1C Powers With Variables

Student Resource pp. 73–74

Teaching Suggestions
Explain that because variables represent numbers the rules do not change when a variable is used rather than a number.

2.1D The Negative Exponent: What Is It?

Student Resource pp. 75–77

Teaching Suggestions
Review the activity on an overhead projector to explain the three ways to describe the meaning of a negative exponent. Establish the pattern numerically as the exponents decrease to from positive to zero to negative values.

Many students find the negative exponent extremely difficult, so do not belabour this concept. The technology will give decimal answers that may be confusing. It is worthwhile to demonstrate that the numbers are getting smaller. Exercise 2 on student resource page 77 returns to the pattern established at the beginning of this activity.

Common Errors
Clarify the difference between a negative base and a negative exponent.

2.1E The Zero Exponent

Student Resource p. 78

Teaching Suggestions

Refer to the chart and pattern established in Activity 2.1D of the student resource.

Common Errors

Students find the zero exponent unusual. It is an abstract concept for most students at this developmental level. Having the students recite aloud, as a class, the phrase, "Anything to the exponent of zero is equal to one," will help.

Section 2.2 Scientific Notation and Exponents

2.2A Using Scientific Notation

Student Resource pp. 79–81

Teaching Suggestions

Have students use scientific calculators to do the first problem without scientific notation. Then, do the problem using scientific notation. Demonstrate the ease that scientific notation can provide for them if they understand it. Demonstrate that scientific notation can also be used as a tool in situations where a calculator will not accept large numbers. Ask the students why they think the picture on student resource page 81 is in this section.

This is a good activity for practising estimation of answers. This activity definitely requires some scientific notation application questions from a resource of your choice.

Common Errors

It will be necessary to clarify the varied forms presented by different scientific calculators.

Assessment

Distribute to the class *Assessment Master 13*, A2.2 Scientific Notation and Exponents: Quiz, and have the students complete it. Collect and mark it for formative assessment.

Specific Expectations
NA2.03

Overall Goals and Key Concepts
- understand the meaning of zero exponent

Timing
20 min

Specific Expectations
NA1.02, NA1.04, NA2.03, NA2.04, NA2.05

Overall Goals and Key Concepts
- use exponents to work with very large and very small numbers

Materials
- *Assessment Master 13* A2.2 Scientific Notation and Exponents: Quiz

Timing
150 min

Related Resources
MATHPOWER 9™, Ontario Edition, Blackline Masters Masters 3.1, 3.3

Section 2.3 Algebra

2.3A Like Terms

Student Resource pp. 82–83

Specific Expectations
NA1.02, NA 3.01, NA 3.02

Overall Goals and Key Concepts
- understand what a variable is
- recognize like terms
- simplify variable expressions

Materials
- overhead algebra tiles
- algebra tiles

Timing
150 min (including extra practice)

Related Resources
MATHPOWER 9™, Ontario Edition, Blackline Masters
Masters 6.1, 6.3, 6.4

Warm Up
Introduce the idea of a variable to represent a number.

Teaching Suggestions
Review with the class Examples 1 and 2 and have the students provide other examples. Use algebra tiles to demonstrate visually the difference between x, y, x^2, x^3, etc. Have the students manipulate algebra tiles to demonstrate adding and subtracting like terms. Using algebra tiles on an overhead, along with one set per student, is most effective. After approximately 20 to 30 minutes with algebra tiles, the students are usually ready to make the transition to paper. At this point, introduce the definition of **like terms**. Direct teaching of collecting like terms is needed. Use algebra tiles. Work through the activity. If necessary, let the students use their calculators to do the arithmetic calculations.

Common Errors
After completing the examples, and before beginning the practice, you may need to review addition and subtraction of integers with the students.

2.3B How to Handle Brackets

Student Resource p. 84

Specific Expectations
NA1.02, NA 3.01, NA 3.02

Overall Goals and Key Concepts
- simplify algebraic expressions by using the distributive property to collect like terms

Materials
- algebra tiles

Timing
150 min (including extra practice)

Related Resources
MATHPOWER 9™, Ontario Edition, Blackline Masters,
Masters 6.4, 6.5
Optional: 6.6, 6.8 (with caution)

Warm Up
Explain that *distribute* means to pass out something. Here, you are "passing out" the term in front of the bracket by multiplying it by each term inside the brackets.

Teaching Suggestions
Let the students use their calculators, if they wish, to do the arithmetic. Use algebra tiles to demonstrate the two equivalent forms i.e., $2(x + 4)$ and $2x + 8$, as shown on student resource page 84. Use examples such as $-(2x + 4)$ to demonstrate the distribution of (-1).

Common Errors
Often, you need to remind the students that the negative sign in front of a term being distributed moves with the term. Review multiplication of integers at this point.

> Nothing succeeds like success
>
> Proverb

2.3C Solving Equations

2.3D Magic Equations: Magic Square

Student Resource pp. 85–87

Specific Expectations
NA1.02, NA 3.03

Overall Goals and Key Concepts
- use balancing to solve equations

Materials
- balance scale
- overhead projector
- overhead algebra tiles
- the game *Hands-On Equations*®

Timing
200 min (including additional practice)

Related Resources
MATHPOWER 9™,
Ontario Edition,
Blackline Masters

Teaching Suggestions

If you can access the game, *Hands-On Equations*®, to teach equation solving, it is very effective. Using the balance approach usually promotes understanding. Bring in a balance scale to class to demonstrate the idea that one side is always to be equal to the other, eventually getting the variable equal to a number. You can simulate a balanced solution to equations by using algebra tiles on the overhead. It is likely you will need to provide supplementary material to practise solving equations for 15 to 20 minutes for the next several days. Checking the solution reinforces the balance approach to equation solving. Students seem to enjoy solving the magic square. They can do it in pairs, and share their answers.

Common Errors

Some students may try to solve the equations in their head. Reward good thinking; then, reinforce the idea of learning this method to be used when mental math does not work, by showing an example that cannot be done mentally.

Specific Expectations
NA1.02, NA2.02, NA3.01, NA3.02, NA3.03

Overall Goals and Key Concepts
- review algebra skills

Timing
45 min

2.3E Algebra: Practice

Student Resource p. 88

Teaching Suggestions
Review with the class the process of substitution and the checking of equations.

Common Errors
Students often do well on collecting like terms and solving equations when they see these separately. In this activity they are combined, so it may be necessary to point out the difference in questions 1–3.

> "Every student is the most important person in the world to someone."
> T. Anne and Rod Yeager

Section 2.4 Slopes

2.4A Slopes of Staircases and Ramps

Student Resource pp. 89-91

Specific Expectations
NA1.03, AG2.01, AG2.02

Overall Goals and Key Concepts
- find the slope by counting squares or measuring rise and run
- give slope a number and relate that number to the slope of the stairs, ramp, or line

Materials
- 1-cm interlocking cubes
- large grid paper
- overhead projector

Timing
75 min

Related Resources
MATHPOWER 9™,
Ontario Edition,
Blackline Masters
Masters 2.1, 2.3 (ratios)

Warm Up

Introduce the idea of slope by leading a discussion about places where slopes are found, and why a number to represent a slope may be needed (roofs, ramps, ski or skateboard hills, mountains, etc.).

Teaching Suggestions

Use 1-cm interlocking cubes to build staircases of varied slopes ($\frac{2}{3}$, 3, ..., and the reverse, $\frac{3}{2}$, $\frac{1}{3}$, etc.). Build some staircases steep and others shallow. Define the slope as $\frac{\text{rise}}{\text{run}}$.

Count the cubes to find rise and run. Substitute these values into the formula, slope $= \frac{\text{rise}}{\text{run}}$. Observe with the class how the result changes, depending on the steepness of the stairs. Have volunteers build, with cubes, staircases with slope 2, 5, $\frac{3}{4}$, etc. Students generally like to do this. It is ideal if each pair of students has cubes to build the staircases.

Draw a staircase on large grid paper. Have a pair of students find its slope by measuring the rise and the run. Revisit Activity 1.6B on student resource pages 60–61 for comparison. Have the students find the slopes of these lines if they have not already done so. Draw a ramp on the chalkboard. Have a pair of students find its slope by measuring the rise and the run. Then, ask a pair of students to draw a staircase (or a ramp) that has a slope of your choice, such as $\frac{4}{5}$ or $\frac{3}{7}$. Now you are ready for the activity. Display student resource page 89 on an overhead projector, and go through some examples with students. Once again, talk about slopes in the real world and the need to know their values (roofs, wheelchair ramps, walking ramps, skateboard ramps, staircases, etc.).

Common Errors

- The idea of a negative slope may be difficult for some students. Revisit positive and negative correlation and relate this to positive and negative slope (ideally, students will recognize this on their own).
- When the scale interval is other than 1, as in question 5, the students need an explanation and to be reminded of how to deal with it.

Specific Expectations
NA1.03, AG2.01, AG2.02

Overall Goals and Key
Concepts
- find the slope and
  communicate it to a
  classmate

Materials
- *Assessment Master 14,*
  A2.4B Slope: Quiz

Timing
40 min

Specific Expectations
NA1.03, AG2.01, AG2.02

Overall Goals and Key
Concepts
- apply slope to a real
  situation

Materials
- measuring tape
- boards
- books

Timing
20 min

Specific Expectations
AG2.01, AG2.02, NA1.03

Overall Goals and Key
Concepts
- find slopes of real stairs
  and ramps

Materials
- boards
- books

Timing
10-min review in class

2.4B Finding Slopes of Stairs

Student Resource pp. 92–93

Teaching Suggestions

This very effective pair-share will consolidate the previous day's ideas. Circulate to be sure that the students are discussing their answers and that they are doing the activity in the pair-share style, that is, one student works while the other coaches. After they have done it as a pair-share they could do alternate questions independently or for homework.

This activity works very well in conjunction with Activity 2.4C, where students go in pairs to find the slope of a ramp in the school.

Assessment

Distribute to the class *Assessment Master 14,* A2.4B Slope: Quiz, and have the students complete it. Collect and mark it for formative assessment.

2.4C Finding Slopes of Ramps

Student Resource p. 94

Teaching Suggestions

This activity can be done in conjunction with Activity 2.4B. Students can go in pairs to find a ramp in the school, take the measurements, and calculate the actual slope. Alternatively, outside of school hours they can find the slope of a ramp in their town or neighbourhood. Provide each pair with a measuring tape and give clear guidelines as to what you expect. If the students cannot leave the classroom because of school rules, etc., then a ramp could be set up within the classroom, using a board and several books to hold up one end. In this way, each pair could have a different ramp and a different slope. You may wish to provide feedback on this work in preparation for Activity 2.4D.

Common Errors

If the students have difficulty, review scale drawing.

2.4D Assignment: Slopes of Stairs and Ramps

Student Resource pp. 95–96

Teaching Suggestions

This is intended to be a take-home assignment. Review your assignment expectations with the students. Be clear about format and due dates, etc. Alternatively, this could be an in-class assessment, where a set of portable stairs is brought into the class and ramps are constructed with a board held up at one end with a stack of books.

Section 2.5 Linear Models

2.5A Modelling Linear Relationships

Student Resource pp. 97–100

Teaching Suggestions

This activity combines many basic concepts of the course. Proceed slowly with the students through Problems 1 and 2, using the overhead projector. Be sure to touch on, and talk about, problem solving, linear modelling, creating a table of values, graphing from a table, making a scatter plot and drawing the line of best fit, finding the slope and intercept and relating them to the problem and the equation, interpolating, identifying parallel lines (same slope), and solving equations. After doing the first problem slowly with the students, some will be able to do the second problem partially on their own. Suggest that they try questions 1 and 2 of problem 2 by themselves, and then go over them. Then, have them continue with question 3, and then go over it, and so on.

Common Errors

This will be the students' first experience with formalizing the meaning of the intercept on the vertical axis. Take the time to discuss this. The coordinates of the point at which the intercept, b, occurs are $(0, b)$. Discuss and compare the point $(0, b)$ with the point $(0, 0)$. Explain that, if the point $(0, b)$ lies on the line, the line represents a partial variation since it does not intersect $(0, 0)$. If the line intersects the point $(0, 0)$, then the line represents a direct variation. This can be connected to the relevance of $(0, 0)$ in hypothesis writing in Unit 1.

2.5B Modelling Linear Relationships: Pair-Share

Student Resource pp. 101–104

Teaching Suggestions

Circulate to be sure students are doing this activity correctly, and as a pair-share. Only one student writes; the other coaches and explains. Then they trade roles. If the students are having difficulty, direct them to Activity 2.5A. Once they have done one problem, they can do the other problem independently in class or for homework.

Assessment

Distribute to the class *Assessment Master 15*, A2.5B Modelling Linear Relationships: Quiz, and have the students complete it. Collect and mark it for formative assessment.

Specific Expectations
AG2.04, AG3.03, AG3.04, RE2.01, RE2.02, RE2.03, RE2.05, RE3.01, RE3.04, NA4.01, NA4.02, NA4.03

Overall Goals and Key Concepts
- create a graphical and algebraic model to describe and solve a problem

Materials
- overhead projector

Timing
75 min

Related Resources
MATHPOWER 9™, Ontario Edition, Blackline Masters Masters 5.3, 5.5 Use with caution. Partial and direct variation will need to be explained. Suggest finding other resources.

Specific Expectations
AG2.03, AG2.04, AG3.04, NA4.01, NA4.02, NA4.03, RE3.01

Overall Goals and Key Concepts
- communicate/explain mathematical modelling

Materials
- *Assessment Master 15*, A2.5B Modelling Linear Relationships: Quiz
- overhead projector
- large grid paper

Timing
40 min

Specific Expectations
NA1.02, AG3.01

Overall Goals and Key Concepts

- extend the idea of coordinates to negative values and using *x* and *y* rather than the concrete

Materials

- *Assessment Master 16, A2.6 The Cartesian Plane: Assignment*
- overhead projector
- large chart paper

Timing
45 min

Related Resources
MATHPOWER 9™, Ontario Edition, Blackline Masters
Masters 1.10, 5.1, 5.2, 5.3

Section 2.6 The Cartesian Plane

Student Resource p. 105

Warm Up

Discuss the map shown on student resource page 105, and how coordinates are used to find a particular place. Ask the students to find John St. and describe where it is. Find some interesting information about René Descartes, or have a student do this, and tell a story about him to the students.

Teaching Suggestions

Place student resource page 105 on an overhead projector, or use large chart paper or a large grid on the chalkboard. Work through the activity with the students. As an additional assignment, have the students make up a picture using a series of straight-line segments, write the coordinates of the end points of the line segments drawn to make the picture, and, then, list the coordinates of the points. Have pairs of students exchange pictures and, then, draw their partner's picture. This assignment is particularly appealing for those students with an interest in art, and provides practice in finding points without the boredom of the drill.

Assessment

Distribute to the class 1-cm grid paper, and *Assessment Master 16, A2.6 The Cartesian Plane: Assignment*, and have the students complete it. Collect and mark it for formative assessment.

Specific Expectations
AG1.01, AG1.02, AG2.03, AG2.04, AG3.03

Overall Goals and Key Concepts

- understand the graphs of linear equations.
- understand slope, *y*-intercept, parallel and perpendicular lines, and families of lines

Materials

- graphing calculators
- graphing software such as *Graphmatica*

Timing
150 min

Related Resources
MATHPOWER 9™, Ontario Edition, Blackline Masters
Master 5.6

Section 2.7 The Equation *y* = *mx* +*b*

2.7A Linear Equations *y* = *mx* +*b* Using Graphing Technology

Student Resource pp. 106–114

Teaching Suggestions

The students will learn a great deal of information from this activity. It works best if students do it in chunks, with time to consolidate the ideas before moving on. A suggested set of breaking points in the form of exercises is provided, but you can be flexible and decide for yourself.

Graphing calculators can be used for this activity. *Graphmatica* and some other computer programs are very effective, and it is easy to read the *y*-intercept and count the squares to find the slope.

Be sure the students are putting answers on their pages, and reading the graphs correctly. When it appears that most students have completed Exercises 1, 2, and 3, recap what they have learned by reviewing some of the questions and providing the students with some additional questions on the chalkboard. This might be a good time to stop and assign homework.

Before doing exercise 4, discuss perpendicular lines with the students. Explain that the resolution on the computer screens may not be perfect or square. On the TI-83 Plus graphing calculator, you can correct this by squaring the grid. Do this after your have graphed your equations by pressing **ZOOM**, then cursoring down to **ZSquare**, and then pressing **Enter**. In *Graphmatica*, the default grid is square, $-7 \leq x \leq 7$, $-4.66 \leq y \leq 4.66$. After most students appear to have finished exercise 4, review it with them. Stop again after exercises 5 and 6 and review the answers with the students. You could stop again until next day, then complete exercise 7. There are numerous exercises and many resources available in other math text books that will provide practice for the students to consolidate these ideas in their daily homework. Linear equations are revisited in Activity 3.7C, using *The Geometer's Sketchpad®*.

Common Errors
- Some students have problems with vertical and horizontal lines. The slope of a vertical line is particularly puzzling to them.
- Students often rely on the technology to answer the questions. Teacher direction is essential for the ideas to be internalized and consolidated.

2.7B Lines and More Lines

Student Resource pp. 115–116

Warm Up
Review with the students the work they learned on the computer in the previous activity. Clarify the meaning of slope and y-intercept and where these numbers appear in the equation in question 1.

Teaching Suggestions
Place the first page of the activity on an overhead projector and go through one or two parts in question 2. Let the students finish question 2 and, then, take up this question with them. Use the steps given at the beginning of question 3 to demonstrate to the students step by step how to graph a line given in slope y-intercept form. Have the students complete the question and then, take it up with them. Use a process similar to this for questions 4–6.

Assessment
Distribute to the class *Assessment Master 17*, A2.7B Slopes and Lines: Quiz, and have the student complete it. Collect and mark it for formative assessment.

"Your title gives you authority, but it's your demonstrated behaviour that actually earns you cooperation and respect."

Harvey Silver and Bart Mindszenthy

Specific Expectations
AG1.03, AG2.03, AG2.04, AG3.04

Overall Goals and Key Concepts
- consolidate ideas learned in previous days on the computer

Materials
- *Assessment Master 17*, A2.7B Slopes and Lines: Quiz
- overhead projector

Timing
75 min

Related Resources
MATHPOWER 9™, Ontario Edition, Blackline Masters
Masters 8.1, 8.3, 8.4 (Omit from Master 8.4 questions 5–8 and 19.), 8.6

2.7C Equations of Lines: Chart

Student Resource p. 117

Teaching Suggestions

Choose a few questions to do with students and let them finish the rest. You could provide the students with grid paper and ask them to include a graph of each equation, or you could have pairs of volunteers come to the front and graph the line using the slope and the y-intercept. Continually ask, "How do you know that the graph of this equation is a straight line? What changes can you make to this equation so that its graph is a curve? What is the y-intercept and how do you know? What is the slope and how do you know?"

Assessment

Distribute to the class *Assessment Master 18*, A2.7C Linear Equations, and have the students complete it. Collect and mark it for formative aseessment.

"Technology is useless without human thought."

T. Anne and Rod Yeager

Specific Expectations
AG1.03, AG2.03, AG2.04, AG3.04

Overall Goals and Key Concepts
• consolidate slope, intercept, and parallel and perpendicular lines

Materials
• *Assessment Master 18*, A2.7C Linear Equations

Timing
40 min

Related Resources
MATHPOWER 9™, *Blackline Masters* Masters 5.4, 8.5 (Rearrange equations 5 and 6 into $y = mx + b$ form.)

2.7D Find the Equation of a Line

Student Resource pp. 118–120

Teaching Suggestions

Draw a few lines on a large grid or on an overhead grid where the slope and y-intercept are easy to read. Find the equations of these lines, explaining to the students how you are doing this. Then work through an example similar to questions 1 to 4 in the activity on student resource page 118. Have the students complete this activity page. Because their answers may vary depending on the accuracy of the drawn line, encourage them to use a pencil or pen with a fine point and to join the points accurately.

Common Errors

Circulate to be sure the students are correctly finding the points and choosing appropriate points to find the slope. Watch for negative slopes.

Assessment

Distribute to the class *Assessment Master 19*, A2.7D Lines and More Lines: Quiz, and have the students complete it. Collect and mark for formative assessment

Specific Expectations
NA4.01, NA4.02, NA4.03, AG2.03, AG2.04, AG3.04, AG3.02

Overall Goals and Key Concepts
• plot points, join them, and find the resulting equation

Materials
• *Assessment Master 19*, A2.7D Lines and More Lines: Quiz
• large grid paper
• overhead projector
• overhead grid

Timing
100 min

2.7E Find the Equation of the Line That Represents the Cost

Student Resource pp. 119–120

Teaching Suggestions

Do question 1 with the students using an overhead projector. Relate this question to what the students learned in Activity 2.7D on student resource page 118 and in Activity 2.5A on student resource pages 97–100. Once again you could discuss partial and direct variation. You could also use the equation of the line, and/or interpolation to find other information. For example: What would be the cost to mow the lawn seven times? What would be the initial fee? Have the students answer part b) of a question on their own, and, then, check their results, before assigning the next question. Have the students create their own questions about the situation that could be answered using the equation or the graph.

Common Errors

As the students complete the graphs, circulate to be sure they choose appropriate scales.

2.7F Graphing Lines: Three Methods

Student Resource pp. 121–122

Warm Up

Write the equation $2x - 3y = 6$ on the chalkboard, and ask the students to find the slope and the y-intercept. Do not belabour this. Note that, unless the equation is in the form $y = mx + b$, the slope and y-intercept are not obvious to the students. Explain that they will learn how to draw the graph of an equation such as this, without rearranging it into slope y-intercept form.

Teaching Suggestions

Show the students the chart for the table of values. Discuss how many points are needed to graph a line. Remind them that two is enough, but three or more is good as a double check. Graph $y = 2x + 5$ using both table of values and y-intercept and slope. Have the students complete exercises 1 to 3. They should get the same line.

Then, teach the students how to find the x- and y-intercepts in order to use Method 3 to graph an equation in the form $ax + by = c.$ Use numbers, not a, b, and c. Do a few examples, and then revisit $2x - 3y = 6$ and have students finish exercises 4 and 5. Discuss under what conditions different methods are easier. Take a few minutes to discuss how to use equation-solving to go from one form of an equation to another, in case any of the students are ready for this. (It is not an expectation, however.)

Common Errors

Some students find all these methods confusing. Focus on the slope y-intercept method of graphing.

Section 2.8 Linear Models for Comparison Shopping

2.8A Example of Comparison Shopping

2.8B Comparison Shopping: Practice

Student Resource pp. 123–126

Specific Expectations
NA4.01, NA4.02, NA4.03, RE3.01, RE3.04, RE2.01, RE2.02, RE 2.03, RE2.05, AG3.05, AG2.03

Overall Goals and Key Concepts
- use linear graphs to solve problems

Materials
- *Teacher Resource Master 13* (Comparison Shopping)
- *Assessment Master 20, A2.8B* Comparison Shopping: Quiz
- overhead projector
- overhead grid
- coloured pens

Timing
100 min

Teaching Suggestions
Review Activity 2.8A on the overhead projector with the class. Have different students complete the charts for the three plans. Suggest that the students use a different colour to draw each line. On the overhead projector, this works well with different coloured pens. Note the points of intersection of the lines, and what they mean in terms of the problem. Discuss how the lowest line at any one point is the least expensive plan for that situation.

Make five copies of *Teacher Resource Master 13* (Comparison Shopping) for each student to do the five problems in Activity 2.8B. You may have to do another example first. In question 5 you could ask the students to comment on parallel lines and the same *y*-intercept and what this means in terms of the question.

Common Errors
Ensure that the students do not increase the scale by 1-unit increments, since they need to get to 30 hours (in the tennis example), and to 200 books (in problem 1).

Assessment
Distribute to the class *Assessment Master 20, A2.8B* Comparison Shopping: Quiz and *Teacher Resource Master 13*, Comparison Shopping, and have the students complete it. Collect and mark it for formative assessment.

Unit 2 Review

Overall Goals and Key Concepts
- clarify and consolidate ideas from Unit 2

Materials
- *Review Masters 1 to 5*

Timing
Five 30-min periods

Teaching Suggestions
The concepts of Unit 2 are challenging enough that a thorough reviews of this unit is warranted before the assessment. Rather than doing all the review at once, consider spending half a period on the assessment and doing some review relevant to the next day's assessment during the second half of the class. This breaks up both the assessment and the review.

Overall Goals and Key Concepts

- summative assessment activity and paper and pencil test

Materials

- *Final Assessment Masters 21 to 24*
- *Final Final Assessment Master 25*
- *Teacher Resource Master 13*, Comparison Shopping

Timing

Five 40-min periods

Final Assessment

Teaching Suggestions

The summative activity is in four parts (*Final Assessment Masters 21 to 24*). If students have the introduction and schedule several days in advance, the attendance and comfort level will improve. Providing the students (a day in advance) with the first page of each of the four parts of the assessment will allow them processing time as well as time to seek the assistance in reading and interpreting which some students require (particularly those with learning disabilities). A letter home with this information can be helpful. *Final Final Assessment Master 25* concludes the assessment for this unit.

"Communication with the home can make the difference between success and failure."

T. Anne and Rod Yeager

A2.1B Exponents: Quiz

1. Write each power in expanded form.

   a) 3^5 = _____

   b) $(-1)^3$ = _____

2. Write each in **exponential form**.

   a) $(2)(2)(2)(2)(2)(2)$ = _____   b) $(-40)(-40)(-40)(-40)$ = _____

   c) $(3)(3)(3)(1.7)(1.7)(1.7)(1.7)$ = _____

3. Place the appropriate name on each blank: (*exponent, base, power*)

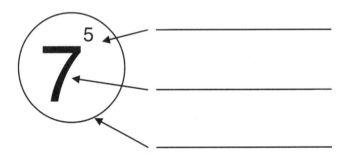

4. Simplify.

   a) $(3)^8(3)^{15}$ = _____   b) $(5)^{10} \div (5)^3$ = _____

   c) $(4^2)^3$ = _____   d) $(2)(2)^{10}(3)^4(3)^5$ = _____

   e) $\dfrac{(3)^4(3)^5}{(3)^2}$ = _____

5. Express each number as a power with the indicated base:

   a) 64 with a base of 2   **b)** 100 000 with a base of 10

6. Explain the difference between 3×4 and 3^4.

7. How would you explain to a friend that $4^7 \div 4^3 = 4^4$?

8. Explain the difference between $(-3)^2$ and -3^2.

A2.2 Scientific Notation and Exponents: Quiz

1. Use your exponent rules to simplify each of the following. Leave all answers with positive exponents.

   a) $3^{12} \times 3^{-4}$ b) $2^2 \div 2^{-5}$ c) $5^{-5} \times 5^{-3}$

   d) $x^3 x^5$ e) $(2y^5)(3y^2)$

2. Explain what the negative means in each question.

   a) $(-4)^3$ b) 4^{-3}

3. Express each of the following in expanded form.

   a) 2.31×10^8 b) $2.31 \div 10^{-8}$

4. Express each of the following in scientific notation.

   a) $2\,500\,000\,000 =$ b) $0.000\,007\,51 =$

5. Use your knowledge of exponents and scientific notation to simplify each expression. Express your answers in scientific notation.

   a) $2.2 \times 10^{18} \times 3 \times 10^6$ b) $300\,000 \div 0.000\,000\,000\,2$

6. A single electron has a mass of 9×10^{-27} g.
   What would be the mass of 1 billion ($1\,000\,000\,000$) electrons?

A2.4B Slope: Quiz

1. State the slope of each staircase.

   a)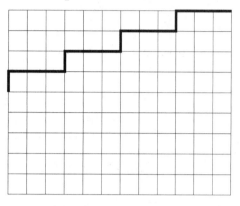

   b)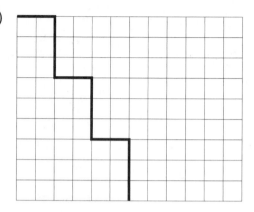

2. State the slope of each line.

   a)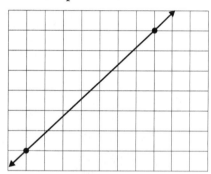

   b)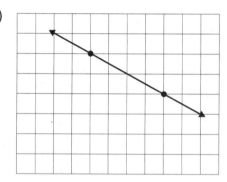

3. This diagram represents a roof. Find its slope.

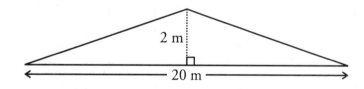

2 m

20 m

4. The slope of a line segment is $\frac{2}{3}$. State two possibilities for the rise and run.

   Possibility 1   Possibility 2

   Rise _____   Rise _____

   Run _____   Run _____

5. There are two line segments, one with slope 3 and one with slope –3.
   a) What would be the same about these 2 line segments?

   b) What would be different about these 2 line segments?

6. To be safe, a wheelchair ramp must have a slope of $\frac{1}{12}$ or less. Check if the
   following wheelchair ramps are safe. Show your work. Explain your answer.
   a)
   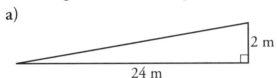
   b)
   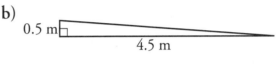

7. Without actually working out each slope, match the line segment with the *most
   likely* correct slope. (Put the letter that corresponds to the line beside the correct
   slope.)

   4 ___   1 ___ $\frac{1}{4}$ ___   0 ___ $-\frac{1}{4}$ ___   –1 ___   –4 ___

   A   B   C   D   E   F   G

8. Hillary snowboards, and always looks for the steepest hills. She
   can choose a hill with a slope of $\frac{8}{5}$ or a hill with a slope of $\frac{5}{8}$.
   Which of these hills do you think she will choose? Explain
   your answer. You may use graph paper if necessary.

A2.5B Modelling Linear Relationships: Quiz

Problem

The cost of a canoe trip with The Canoe Company is $200 for the guide, plus $25 per day. The total cost can be modelled by the equation $C = 25d + 200$.

1. Create a table of values showing the total charges for a trip that could take up to 10 days.

2. Graph the relation.

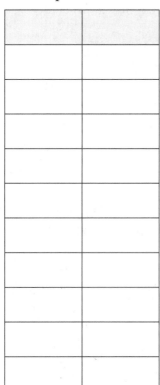 

3. a) Identify the slope and the C-intercept of your line.

   b) How do these relate to the cost of the trip? (Show any necessary work.)

   Slope   How it relates

   C-intercept   How it relates

4. If the total cost of a trip was $275, for how many days was the trip? (Note that it is possible to be on a trip for part of a day, and charged for that fraction of the day.) Explain your answers or show your work.

5. a) If the cost of the guide remained the same, but the Canoe Company changed the daily rate to $30, how would the graph change?

  b) Write the new equation that would represent the total cost.

  _____

6. The Trail Company, another company, made a graph of its charges. This graph lay at the same angle as the Canoe Company, but its cost for a guide was $300.

  a) Describe what this means in terms of the total cost of a trip with the Trail company. Be specific.

  b) Write the equation that models the total cost of a trip with the Trail Company.

  _____

A2.6 The Cartesian Plane: Assignment

1. Draw a picture, or print your name or your initials on the grid provided, using only straight-line segments. Be sure to have the end points of each line segment on a point where the grid lines intersect. Use all 4 quadrants.

2. Write, in the order in which they would be connected, the coordinates of the end points of each line. Write the coordinates as sets. Begin a new set if the line segments do not connect.

3. Make your picture interesting, but not cluttered, by adding simple detail and some colour.

Marking Checklist

Item	Possible Marks	Marks Earned
Picture/letters and endpoints clear, used all 4 quadrants	5	
Coordinates correct	5	
Sets of coordinates correct	5	
Colour and detail added for interest, but not over done	5	

TOTAL: _____/20

A2.7B Slopes and Lines: Quiz

1. For each of the following equations answer the questions given below.
    (Equations may be used more than once.)

    A: $y = 3x + 1$ B: $y = -2x + 3$ C: $y = -x - 2$

    D: $y = 3x - 4$ E: $y = 2x + 1$ F: $y = x + 4$

    a) Which lines are parallel? _____

    b) Which lines are at 90° to each other (*perpendicular*)? _____

    c) Which lines cross the *y*-axis at the same point? _____

2. Use your knowledge of slope and
    y-intercept to help you draw the
    graph of each line.
    a) $y = -2x + 3$
    b) $y = 3x - 4$

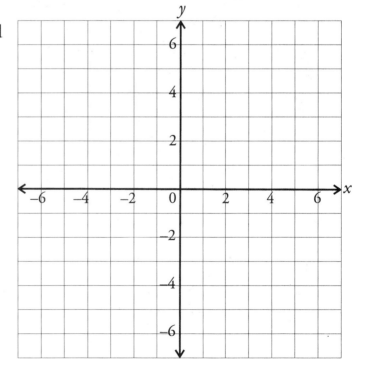

3. Circle the following equations that represent non-linear graphs.

    A: $y = -2 + x$ B: $y = 3x^2$ C: $y = \frac{3}{2}x - 5$

    D: $x = y^3 + 3$ E: $2x + 5y = 8$ F: $x^2 + y^2 = 9$

A2.7C   Linear Equations: Quiz

Write the equation of each graph in the form $y = mx + b$.

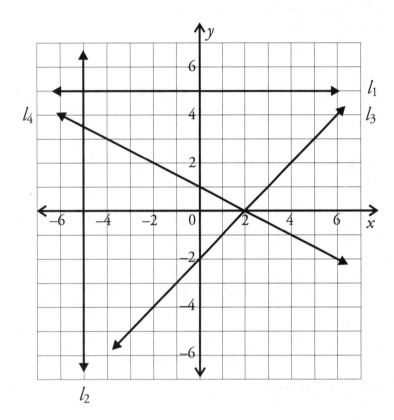

$l_1 = $ _____

$l_2 = $ _____

$l_3 = $ _____

$l_4 = $ _____

A2.7D Lines and More Lines: Quiz

1. An equation of a line is written $y = mx + b$, where m is the _____

   and b is the _____.

2. Complete the following chart.

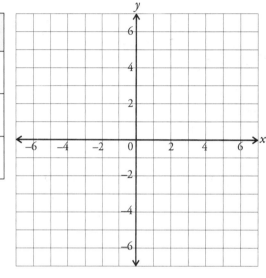

	Equation	Slope	y-intercept
a)	$y = 3x + 1$		
b)	$y = -2x - 5$		
c)		-2	-3

3. Graph the lines in question 2 above, using the slope and y-intercept. Label each line.

4. State any lines that are parallel or perpendicular.

   _____

   Explain how you know.
   ("It looks like it is." is not an acceptable answer.)

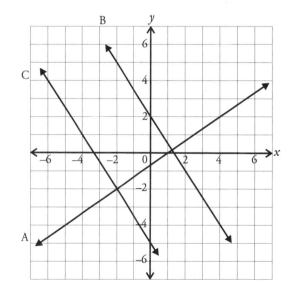

5. Join points A(3, –2) and B(–3, 2).
   Write the equation of line AB.

   _____

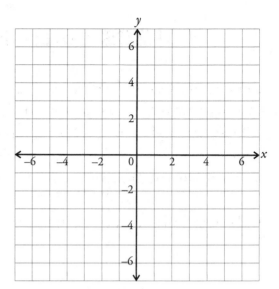

6. a) Lines parallel to $y = \frac{1}{2}x + 5$ have a

   slope of _____.

   b) Write the equation of a line that is
      parallel to the line in a).

   _____.

   c) Graph both lines to show that they
      are parallel.

7. a) Lines perpendicular to $y = -3x + 5$

   have a slope of _____.

   b) Write the equation of a line that is
      perpendicular to the line in a).

   _____.

   c) Graph both lines to show they are
      perpendicular.

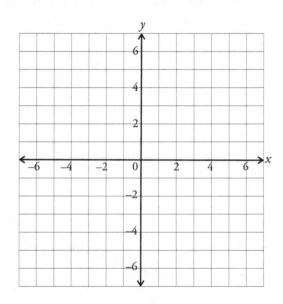

A2.8B Comparison Shopping: Quiz

You plan to do some landscaping around your house. You call Lawns R Us for a price. It charges $240 for a full landscape plan, plus $30/h to do the work. You also call Clean and Green for a price. It charges $60/h for the work, which includes the landscape plan.

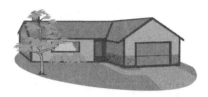

1. Which company do you think is less expensive? Give reasons.

2. Write an equation that represents the charges for each company. Use C for total charges and h for the number of hours of work.

   Lawns R Us: _____

   Clean and Green: _____

3. Complete the Comparison Shopping master provided by your teacher for up to 20 h of work for the two landscape companies.

4. Conclusions: Which landscape company is less expensive to hire? Consider all situations.

5. What other things, besides costs, might you consider when choosing a landscape company?

Review Part 1: Finding Slopes

1. A ramp that is safe for wheelchairs is one with a slope that is no greater than $\frac{1}{10}$.
   Determine whether or not each of the following ramps is safe.
   Show your work and explain your answer.

a)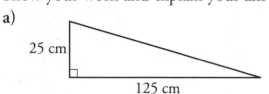

25 cm

125 cm

b)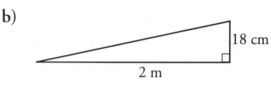

18 cm

2 m

2. Plot each pair of points, draw a line through them and find the slope of the line.
   a) (2, 3), (–5, 0)   b) (2, –4), (–3, 3)   c) (0, 3), (–4, 0)

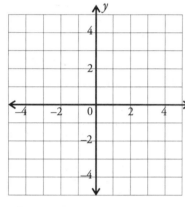

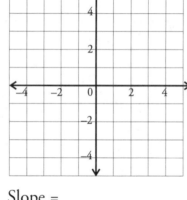

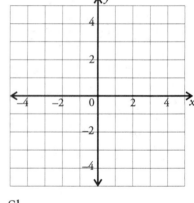

Slope =   Slope =   Slope =

3. For each of the lines in the grid at the right
   a) choose two points on the line and write
      their coordinates
   b) draw a triangle showing the rise and
      the run
   c) find the slope of each line

   Line A: _____

   Line B: _____

   Line C: _____

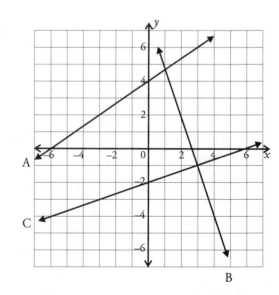

Review Part 2: Find the Cost

1. A carpet cleaning company charges $40 for supplies plus $15 per room.
   a) Write the equation for the total cost.

   $C =$ _____

   b) Find the total cost to clean the carpets in 4 rooms.
   Show your work.

2. The cost of printing books is $1000 for the setup plus $5 per book.
   a) Write the equation for the total cost.

   $C =$ _____

   b) Find the total cost of printing 300 books.
   Show your work.

3. The total cost of printing flyers is $5 for the setup plus $0.10 per copy.
   a) Write the equation for the total cost.

   $C =$ _____

   b) Find the total cost of printing 10 000 flyers.
   Show your work.

4. a) Complete a table of values for the cost of carpet cleaning for up to
     8 rooms in question 1 on the previous page.
   b) Draw a graph of the total cost of cleaning carpets.

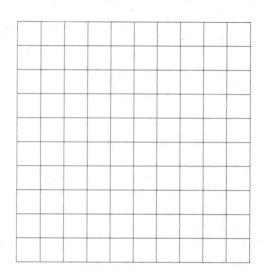

   c) What is the value of the slope? _____
   d) How does the slope relate to the question?

   e) What is the *C*-intercept? _____
   f) How does the *C*-intercept relate to the question?

5. A second carpet cleaning company charges $30 for supplies plus $19 per room.
   a) Write the equation for the cost with this second company.

   b) On the grid in question 4 above, draw a graph to represent the total cost of
     cleaning carpets for this second company. Label the graph.
   c) Describe how the graph in this question is
     different from the graph in question 4.
     Explain the differences.

   d) Which company charges less? Consider all the cases.

Review Part 3: Lines

1. State the equation of each line on the graph shown.

   A: _____

   B: _____

   C: _____

   D: _____

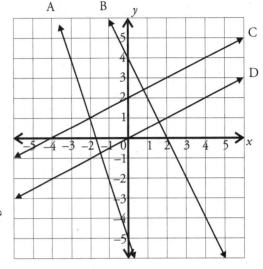

2. a) Which lines in question 1 above are parallel?

   _____ and _____
   Use the equations to explain your answer.

   b) Which lines in question 1 above are perpendicular?

   _____ and _____
   Use the equations to explain your answer.

3. Graph the following lines.

   a) $y = -\frac{2}{3}x + 3$

   b) $y = 2x - 1$ c) $y = \frac{1}{2}x$

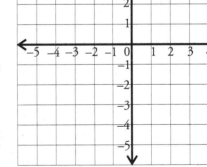

4. a) State the equation of any line parallel to the line in question 3a).

   _____

   b) State the equation of any line perpendicular to the line in question 3b).

   _____

   c) State the equation of any line with the same y-intercept as the line in question 3c).

   _____

Review Part 4: Algebra

1. Simplify.

   a) $5x - 4 + 3x + 7$

   b) $-2y + 5x - y - 8x$

   c) $2m + 5m - m + 3k$

   d) $4(3m + 1) - 2(5 - 2m)$

   e) $2(5z - 2) + 4(3z + 4)$

   f) $3x^2 - 4s - x^2 + 5s$

   g) Evaluate your answer in b) if $x = 3$ and $y = -2$.

2. Solve each equation. Show the steps.

   a) $3x - 4 = 21$

   b) $4m + 11 = 2m + 17$

   c) $3(2x - 5) = 4(3x + 1)$

   d) $3m - 2 + 4m = 13$

   e) $5x - 12 = 3x + 3$

   f) Check your answer for b).

3. Graph and label each equation.

a) $y = \frac{1}{2}x - 3$

b) $y = -3x + 1$

c) $y = 4$

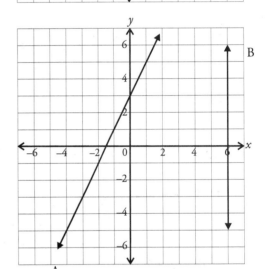

4. a) Write the equation of lines A and B on the second grid.

A: _____

B: _____

b) Join $(-1, 3)$ and $(1, -3)$.
Write the equation of this line.

_____

5. a) Graph the line $y = 4x + 2$.
b) Write the equation of a line parallel to the line in a).

_____

c) Graph your line from b).
Check that it is parallel to the line from a).
d) Write the equation of a line perpendicular to the line from a).

_____

e) Graph the line from d). Check that it is perpendicular to the line from a).
f) Write the equation of a line that has the same y-intercept as the line from a).

_____

g) Graph the line in f). Check that it has the same y-intercept as the line in a).

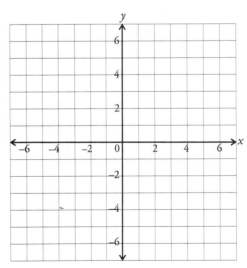

Review Part 5: Exponents

1. Simplify each expression using exponent rules.
   a) $3^4 \times 3^8$
   b) $7^6 \times 7^4$

   c) $4^7 \times 4^6$
   d) $2^5 \times 2^4 \times 2^6$

   e) $6^5 \times 6^4 \times 6^7$
   f) $5^4 \times 5^4 \times 5^5$

   g) $2^5 \times 3^3 \times 2^2 \times 3^1$
   h) $2^5 \times 2^{-3} \times 2^2 \times 2^{-1}$

2. Simplify each of the following using exponent rules.
   a) $3^9 \div 3^8$
   b) $7^6 \div 7^4$

   c) $4^7 \div 4^6$
   d) $8^{20} \div 8^9$

   e) $2^5 \div 2^4$
   f) $5^4 \div 5^4$

   g) $6^5 \div 6^{-4}$
   h) $2^5 \div 3^4$

3. Simplify each expression. Use exponent rules. Do not evaluate.
   a) $(2^3)^5$
   b) $(3^3)^4$

   c) $(3^4)^4(5^3)^5$
   d) $(2^{-3})^{-4}(2^3)^2$

4. Simplify.
   a) $x^7 x^3$
   b) $x^5 \div x^2$

   c) $y^4 y^7$
   d) $j^4 \div j^2$

   e) $c^5 \div c^{-2}$
   f) $z^3 s^4 z^{-1} s^4$

   g) $(m^{-5})^{-2}$
   h) $(q^6)^2(q^4)$

Unit 2 Final Assessment: Introduction
Relations and Algebra

Denis is having his car repaired. He needs the use of a car to go to work and to take a holiday. He is making plans to rent a car and also considering other options if his car is not repaired soon.

Each of the following 4 parts involve some aspect of his need for a car. You will be given information daily that can be taken home to allow preplanning for the following day's activity. This will include reading, interpreting and understanding the problem to be solved in class.

The final part of the assessment will involve a test on:

- like terms
- substitution
- exponents
- equations
- $y = mx + b$
- scientific notation

Part 1: Let's Rent a Car

Denis is considering renting a new car while his is being repaired. He has found the following plans for renting a new model car called a "Ride About." No plan has an additional charge for the distance travelled.

Rental Plan 1: Rent a Ride About for $30 per day.
Rental Plan 2: Rent a Ride About for $20 per day plus an initial fee of $50
Rental Plan 3: Rent a Ride About for a flat rate of $200 for up to 14 days, $200 more for the next 14 days, and so on

1. Use the Comparison Shopping master, provided by your teacher, to collect and organize the data for the total charges for up to 20 days of renting a car for all 3 rental plans.

2. Display these data on the graph. Use one grid, and label carefully (Hint: use a different colour for each rental plan.)

3. Express Rental Plans 1 and 2 using an equation. Use *C* for the total charges and *d* for the number of days of rental.

Rental Plan 1: _____

Rental Plan 2: _____

Conclusions
Use your equations and/or graphs for all three plans to answer the following questions.

1. If Denis wants to rent the car for 4 days, which rental plan do you think he should use? Explain.

2. If Denis wants to rent the car for 7 days, which rental plan do you think he should use? Explain.

3. If Denis wants to rent the car for 12 days, which rental plan do you think he should use? Explain.

4. Make conclusions about the least expensive rental plan. Consider different lengths of rental time when answering.

5. This advertisement appears in a newspaper. Why would Denis not consider this plan?

RENT A
RIDE ABOUT
$450 FOR UP
TO 14 DAYS!

SPECIAL

A2B
CAR RENTALS

6. Should Denis consider other things besides cost when choosing a plan for renting a car? Explain your answer.

Part 2: How Much Gas Is Needed?

Denis goes camping in his rented car. He is interested in the rate of fuel consumption of the car. The odometer readings below show the distance travelled in kilometres, and the fuel gauge readings at each of the eighth markings show how much fuel is in the tank. Denis records his readings as shown below.

1. Make a hypothesis that describes the relationship between the distance travelled, in kilometres, and the fuel gauge reading. Use the descriptors: linear, non-linear, correlation, origin, etc.

   ☞

   ☞

   ☞

   ☞

   ☞

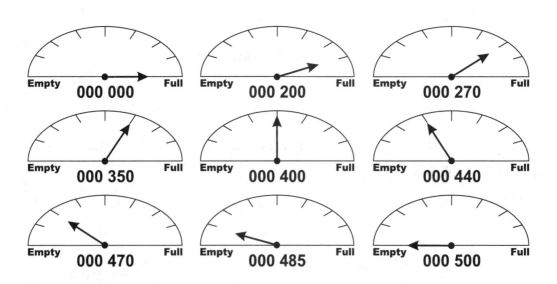

2. Create a table of values using the distance travelled in kilometres, as the independent variable (horizontal axis) and the fuel gauge reading as the dependent variable (vertical axis).

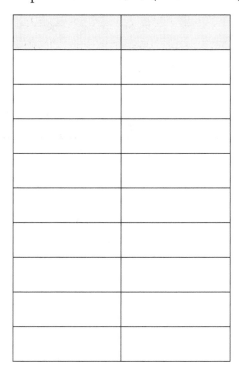

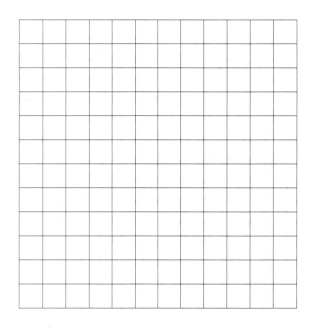

3. Make a scatter plot on the grid given and draw the curve/line of best fit. Be sure to choose an appropriate scale.
    Use your data and graph to answer the following questions.

4. Was your hypothesis correct? If not, make corrections.

5. Does the fuel gauge seem to be accurate? Explain.

6. Use your graph. What do you think the fuel gauge will indicate after Denis has driven 410 km ? _____

    Explain your answer.

7. When the fuel gauge is $\frac{3}{5}$ full, what do you think the odometer will read? _____ Explain your answer.

8. How far do you think Denis can travel on a full tank of gas? _____

9. a) Denis is thinking of taking a trip to Prince Edward Island in this rental car. If the trip is 2500 km each way, how many tanks of gas do you think he will use on his trip? _____ Show your work.

Newfoundland and Labrador

Québec

Ontario

Prince Edward Island

Nova Scotia

New Brunswick

   b) Do you think he will use more tanks of gas than this? Explain.

10. Make up a question of your own that can be answered using the information given. Answer your question.

Part 3: Storing Your Antique Car

Denis has an antique car that he uses at car shows only. He needs to find a place to store it when it is not in use. The Store-It-Here company and the Stay-With-Us company have the following plans.

The Store-It-Here company charges $20 per month plus a registration fee of $150.

Two of Denis' friends use the Stay-With-Us company. One friend told Denis that he paid $650 for 20 months of storage. The other friend told Denis that she paid $200 for 5 months of storage.

Use the information above to complete the questions.

1. Make a graph of the relationship between the number of months and the cost of storage, in dollars, for the Stay-With-Us company and the Store-It-Here company, for up to 2 years of storage. (Assume both relationships are linear.) Label your graph carefully.

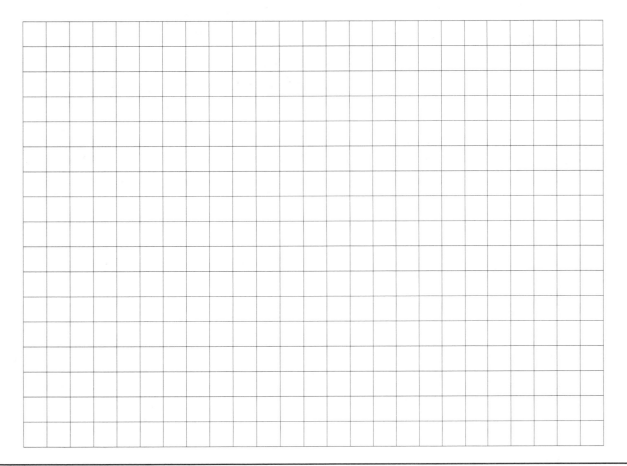

2. Write an equation that represents the charges for storage for each company. Use *C* for the charges, in dollars, and *m* for the number of months of storage.

   Store-It-Here _____

   Stay-With-Us _____

3. Make up a flyer for the Store-It-Here company. Include the registration cost and the cost per month.

4. Denis estimates that his car requires 6 to 10 months of storage per year. Fill out the following chart for the cost of each company if Denis uses storage for 2 years for the lengths of time given.

Company	Cost for 6 Months in a Year ($)	Cost for 10 Months in a Year ($)
Store It Here		
Stay With Us		

5. When will Denis choose Store-It-Here rather than Stay-With-Us if he always chooses the least expensive plan?

   _____ Explain.

6. What other things besides cost might Denis consider when choosing a place to store his antique car.

Part 4: Other Possibilities

Denis' car is being repaired and will not be ready for 2 weeks. He is researching other methods of transportation by collecting advertisements and making some quick graphs.

For each of the following situations,
- circle the descriptors which would best describe the graphs if drawn.
- explain how you know that this is the correct descriptor.

You do not need to actually draw the graph unless it helps you understand or describe your answer.

1. Advertisements for daily taxi service to work show these plans.

   Plan A: $5 per day
   Plan B: $5 per day plus a one-time fee of $10 for an air
           conditioned taxi
   Plan C: $5 per day plus a one-time fee of $100 for a limousine

   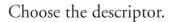

   Choose the descriptor.
   - linear/non linear
     Explain how you know.

   - positive/negative
     Explain how you know.

   - set of parallel lines (yes or no)
     Explain how you know.

   - set of lines that all pass through the same point (yes or no)
     Explain how you know.

   Which plan would you choose and why?

Final Assessment Master 24 **93**

2. Advertisements for the rental of a mountain bike show these options.

Company A: $50 for bike insurance plus $2.50 per day
Company B: $50 for bike insurance plus $3.00 per day
Company C: $50 for bike insurance plus $3.50 per day

Choose the descriptor.
- linear/non linear
  Explain how you know.

- positive/negative
  Explain how you know.

- set of parallel lines (yes or no)
  Explain how you know.

- set of lines that all pass through the same point (yes or no)
  Explain how you know.

3. Another option is walking with a personal stereo to help pass the time. But the batteries can be a problem. They work well for the first 3 h then, the energy quickly drops off. After 4 h, the batteries are dead.

Choose the descriptor.
- linear/non linear
  Explain how you know.

- positive/negative
  Explain how you know.

What kind of batteries do you buy and why?

4. Consider this relationship.
   the distance from work vs. the number of minutes you have walked away from
   home. (Assume that you walk at a constant rate.)

   Choose the descriptor.
   • linear/non linear
     Explain how you know.

   • positive/negative
     Explain how you know.

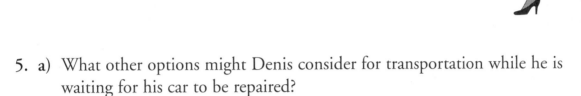

5. **a)** What other options might Denis consider for transportation while he is
   waiting for his car to be repaired?

   b) What option do you think is best for Denis? Explain.

Unit 2 Final Final Assessment

For all the questions, write the complete solutions in the blank spaces provided.

1. Simplify each expression.

   a) $3x + 2 - 4x + 6$ b) $2(2a - 3b) + 5(4a - b)$

2. Simplify, then, evaluate $3(x + y) + 2y - 5x$ if $x = 3$ and $y = -2$.

3. Simplify.

   a) 5^{-2} b) $\left[\dfrac{2}{3}\right]^3$ c) $2^5(2^{-3})$

   d) $\dfrac{5^6 4^7}{4^2 5^3}$ e) $x^5 x^4$ f) $(-3y^2)(2y^3)^3$

4. Solve each equation.

   a) $3x - 5 = 4$ b) $5w + 5 = 3w - 7$

   c) $4(5x - 3) = 8$ d) Check your answer in b).
                                              (Use substitution.)

5. Draw the graph of each linear equation on the grid provided.

   a) $y = -3x + 2$

   b) $y = \frac{4}{5}x - 3$

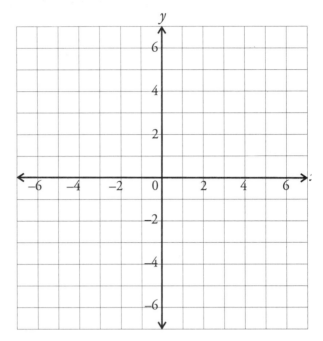

6. a) Write the equations for lines A and B.

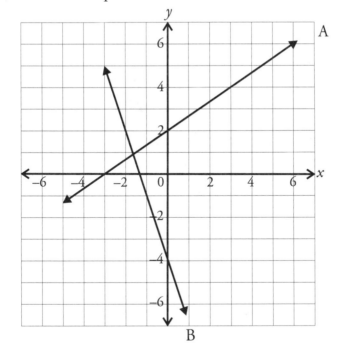

Line A:

Slope (m) = _____

y-intercept (b) = _____

Equation = _____

Line B:

Slope (m) = _____

y-intercept (b) = _____

Equation = _____

   b) Plot the points C(3, 1) and D(–1, –7).
   Write the equation of the line passing through these two points

   _____

7. The equation of a line is $y = 5x - 7$.
   a) State the equation of a line *parallel* to this line.

   _____

   b) State the equation of a line *perpendicular* to this line.

   _____

   c) State an equation of a line with the same *y*-intercept as this line.

   _____

8. A safe ramp for a wheelchair requires a slope of ___ or less.

   Does the following ramp meet the safety standards? Explain.

   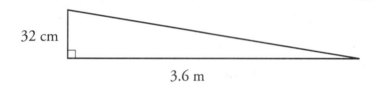

   32 cm

   3.6 m

9. Scientific Notation
   a) Write 4.2×10^{-6} in expanded form.   b) Write 891 000 000 in scientific notation.

   _____   _____

   c) Simplify by expressing each number in scientific notation and then using exponent rules.

   (0.000 002 1)(400 000 000) =

10. Light travels through space at 300 000 000 m/s. If there are 31 600 000 s in one year, how far will light travel through space in one year?

Student Resource Answers

Unit 2   Algebra and Relations

2.1 Exponents pp. 66–78

2.1A Exponents: Introduction pp. 66–68

1. a), b), c), d)

Number of Times Folded Into Halves	Total Number of Sections	$2^{\text{number of times folded}}$ = number of sections
0	1	$2^0 = 1$
1	2	$2^1 = 2$
2	4	$2^2 = 4$
3	8	$2^3 = 8$
4	16	$2^4 = 16$
5	32	$2^5 = 32$
6	64	$2^6 = 64$

2. There is a positive, non-linear relationship between the number of times folded and the number of sections.

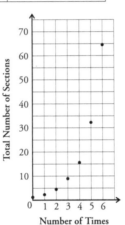

Total Number of Sections vs Number of Times Folded Into Halves

3. a) 256
    b) 1024
4. a), b), c), d)
    Total Number of Sections: 1, 3, 9, 27, 81, 243, 729
    Number of Sections: $3^0 = 1$, $3^1 = 3$, $3^2 = 9$, $3^3 = 27$, $3^4 = 81$, $3^5 = 243$, $3^6 = 729$

5. There is a positive, non-linear relationship between the number of times and the total number of sections.

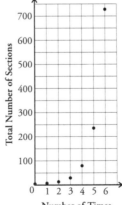

Total Number of Sections vs Number of Times Folded Into Thirds

6. a) 6561
    b) 59 049

Exponents in the Real World: Exponential Growth

Example 1

$50(8) = 400$
$50(2)^4 = 50(16)$
$\qquad = 800$
After 7 h there are $50(2)^7 = 50(128)$
$\qquad\qquad\qquad\qquad = 6400$

$50(2)^n$ bacteria

Example 2

$10(3)^2 = 10(9)$
$\qquad = 90$
$10(3)^3 = 10(27)$
$\qquad = 270$
After 4 hours there are $10(3)^4 = 10(81)$
$\qquad\qquad\qquad\qquad = 810$

$10(3)^n$ insects

2.1B Understanding Powers: Exponent Rules pp. 69–72

Example 1

$5 \times 5 \times 5 \times 5 \times 5 \times 5 \times 5$

Example 2

$2 \times 2 \times 2 \times 2 \times 2$
$2 \times 2 \times 2$
$2 \times 2 \times 2 \times 2 \times 2 \times 2 \times 2 \times 2 = 2^8$
same, base, add, leave

Practice

1. a) 3^{12} b) 7^{10} c) 4^{13}
    d) 8^{29} e) 5^5 f) 3^1
2. a) 2^{15} b) 5^{13} c) 6^{16}
    d) 2^{15} e) $2^5 \times 3^4 \times 4^6$ or $2^{17} \times 3^4$
    f) 2^5
3. a) 2^3 b) $2^7 \times 3^4$ c) $5^9 \times 2^3$
    d) $3^7 \times 2^2$ e) $4^4 \times 2^1$ or 2^9
    f) $2^4 \times 3^3 \times 4^2$ or $2^8 \times 3^3$

Division of Powers

Example 1

Thus, $5^6 \div 5^4$ means $5^{6-4} = 5^2$

Example 2
2^8 means $2 \times 2 \times 2 \times 2 \times 2 \times 2 \times 2 \times 2$
2^3 means $2 \times 2 \times 2$
Thus, $2^8 \div 2^3$ means $2^{8-3} = 2^5$
same, base, subtract, keep

Practice
a) 3 b) 2 c) 7^2 d) 5^0
e) 4 f) 6^9 g) 8^{11} h) $2^5 \div 3^4$
i) 5^9 j) 3^9

Power of a Power

Example 1
5^{18}; 5^{18}

Example 2
2^{12}; 2^{12}
multiply, keep

Practice
a) 2^{15} b) 3^{12} c) 4^{21} d) 2^{24}
e) 5^{27} f) 2^{20} g) $3^{16} \times 5^{15}$ h) 2^{18}

2.1C Powers With Variables
pp. 73–74

Example 1
Add the exponents and keep the bases the same.

Example 2
$x^8 \div x^3 = (x)(x)(x)(x)(x)(x)(x)(x) \div (x)(x)(x)$
$= x5$
Subtract the exponents and keep the base the same.

Example 3
$(x^3)^5 = (x^3)(x^3)(x^3)(x^3)(x^3)$
$= (x)(x)(x)(x)(x)(x)(x)(x)(x)(x)(x)(x)(x)(x)(x)$
$= x^{15}$
Multiply the exponents and keep the base the same.

Practice
1. a) x^{10} b) x^3 c) c^7 d) y^{11}
   e) m^2 f) m^{20} g) $n^9 b^{11}$ h) $z^4 s^8$
   i) m^{10} j) q^8 k) 128^x l) $v^8 b^4$
2. Answers will vary.

2.1D The Negative Exponent: What Is It?
pp. 75–77

Answer 1

Power	2^4	2^3	2^2	2^1	2^0	2^{-1}	2^{-2}	2^{-3}	2^{-4}
Value	16	8	4	2	1	$\frac{1}{2}$	$\frac{1}{4}$	$\frac{1}{8}$	$\frac{1}{16}$

Conclusion A power with a negative exponent is equal to the reciprocal of the base of the power and the exponent positive. The power 2^{-3} is equal to the reciprocal of the base, 2, and the negative exponent, −3, written as its opposite, 3.

1. a) 0.03 b) 0.06 c) 0.13
   d) 0.25 e) 0.5 f) 1

2. a) $\frac{1}{2^5}$ b) $\frac{1}{2^4}$ c) $\frac{1}{2^3}$
   d) $\frac{1}{2^2}$ e) $\frac{1}{2^1}$ f) 2^0

3. x^{-n} is defined to be the reciprocal of x^n, or
   $$x^{-n} = \frac{1}{x^n}$$

4. a) $\frac{1}{4^2}$ b) $\frac{1}{3^3}$ c) $\frac{1}{x^5}$
   d) 2^3 e) $\frac{1}{5^2}$ f) $\frac{1}{5} \times \frac{1}{2^2}$

5. a) $\frac{1}{4^3}$ b) $\frac{1}{3^3}$
   c) $\frac{1}{5^6}$ d) $\frac{1}{6^1}$

2.1E The Zero Exponent
pp. 78

1; 1; 1; 1
Powers with zero exponents equal 1
a) 1 b) 2^5 c) 1
d) 2^8 e) 5 f) $y^3 x^9$

2.2 Scientific Notation and Exponents
pp. 79–81

2.2A Using Scientific Notation
pp. 79–81

Example 1
Answers may vary depending on calculator; for example, 4.8E16 or 4.8 16.

Example 2
7, 6; 7, 6; 13
Answers may vary depending on calculator; for example, 7.2E13

Example 3
7, 6

Example 4
2.4, 2
Answers may vary depending on calculator; for example, 1.2E13; Yes

Example 5

$10, 3, 3; 2.4 \div 3, 10^{10} \div 10^3; 8 \times 10^6$

Example 6

$1.2, 13, -10; 1.2 \div 3, 10^{13} \div 10^{-10}; 4 \times 10^{22}$

More Exponents and Scientific Notation

Example 1

$13, -10; 3; 3; 4$

Example 2

$13, -10; 33.6, 3; 3.36 \times 10^1, 3; 3.36, 4$

Example 3

$13, 4.2, 10; 30.24, 23; 3.024 \times 10^1, 23; 3.024, 24$

Example 4

$10, -10; 2, 20$

Example 5

$1.25, 11, 2.5, -10; 0.5, 21; 5, 20$

Example 6

$10, 8.4, -10; 0.5, 20; 5, 19$

Example 7

$$= (4.2 \times 10^{10}) \div (1.26 \times 10^{-7})$$
$$= (4.2 \div 1.26) \div (10^{10} \times 10^{-7})$$
$$= 3.33 \times 10^{17}$$

2.3 Algebra
pp. 82–88

2.3A Like Terms
pp. 82–83

Example 1	Example 2
$10, 420$	$120; 3y, -y; 5x^2$

Practice

1. a) $12x$ b) $5x^2 + 2x$
   c) $2y + 5$ d) $4y^2 + 3y + 5$
   e) $3x + 3$ f) $2y^2 + 5y$
2. Answers will vary; for example, $2x^2, 4x^2, 5x^2$
3. Answers will vary; for example, $xy, -2xy, 5xy$
4. $3x, -2x, -5x, -2000x, -(3)(-5)x$
5. The variables are not exactly the same. x^2 means $(x)(x)$ and $2(x)$ means $(2)(x)$. The variables are clearly different.

2.3B How to Handle Brackets
p. 84

Example 2	Example 3
$6x + 10$	$-6x - 12$

Example 4	Example 5
$6x^2 - 8x$	$5x + 20 + 8x + 2 = 13x + 22$

Example 6

$6x^2 + 8x - 4x - 16 = 6x^2 + 4x - 16$

Example 7

$-6x^2 + 12x - x^2 - 3x - 5 = -7x^2 + 9x - 5$

2.3C Solving Equations
pp. 85–86

Example 3	Example 4
$x = 4$	$x = 8$

Example 5	Example 6
$x = -2$	$x = -13$

Example 7	Example 8
$x = -17$	$x = 2$

2.3D Magic Equations: Magic Square
p. 87

8	29	30	2
18	14	13	24
11	22	20	16
32	4	6	27

2.3E Algebra: Practice
p. 88

1. a) $8x + 5$ b) $-8y - 2x$ c) $10m + 9k$
   d) $-2x^2 + 3s$ e) $8m - 2$ f) $15z + 9$
2. 10
3. a) $x = 13$ b) $m = 2$ c) $x = -15$
   d) $m = 3$ e) $x = -\dfrac{9}{5}$

2.4 Slopes
pp. 89–96

2.4A Slopes of Staircases and Ramps
pp. 89–91

1. a) $1, 1, \dfrac{1}{1} = 1$ b) $1, 2, \dfrac{1}{2}$
   c) $2, 3, \dfrac{3}{2}$ d) $2, 1, \dfrac{2}{1} = 2$
2. a) $1.8, 3.1, 0.58$ b) $0.9, 3.6, 0.25$
   c) $1.9, 3.1, 0.61$ *   d) $2.6, 4.4, 0.59$
3. a) $6, 4, \dfrac{3}{2}$ b) $1, 3, \dfrac{1}{3}$
   c) $1, 4, \dfrac{1}{4}$ d) $6, 2, 3$
4. A positive slope represents a positive correlation, a negative slope represents a negative correlation. The steeper the line is, the greater is the correlation.
5. A $-6, 2, -3$; B $4, 3, \dfrac{4}{3}$;

   C $-3, 4, -\dfrac{3}{4}$; D $0, 5, 0$

6. a) $100, 4, \frac{1}{25}$.   b) $-50, 3, \frac{-50}{3}$

   c) $2000, 15, \frac{2000}{15} = \frac{400}{3}$

7. greater

2.4B Finding Slopes of Stairs   pp. 92–93

1. a) $\frac{5}{2}$ b) $\frac{3}{4}$

2. a) $\frac{2}{5}$ b) $-\frac{3}{2}$

3. a) $\frac{1}{6}$ b) $\frac{1}{30}$

4. a) $\frac{2}{3}$ b) $\frac{2}{3}$ c) The slope of the line will always be the same.

5. a)   b)

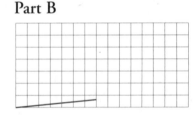

6. C, G, B, D, F, E, A

2.4C Finding Slopes of Ramps   p. 94

All answers will vary; for example:

Part A   **Part B**
rise = 0.5;
run = 7.0

Part C $\frac{1}{14}$

Part D Yes, this ramp has a slope that is less than $\frac{1}{12}$.
$\frac{1}{14} < \frac{1}{12}$

Thus, it passes the safety code.

2.4D Assignment: Slopes of Stairs and Ramps   pp. 95–96

All answers will vary; for example:

1. b) 132

2. rise = 15 cm; run = 24 cm

3. $\frac{5}{8} = 0.625$

5. Yes, $0.625 < 0.667$, i.e., the slope of the stairs is 0.625, which is less than the slope of 0.667, which is safe for children.

7. rise = 0.7 m; run = 10 m

8. $\frac{7}{100} = 0.07$

9.

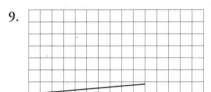

10. Yes, the slope of this ramp is 0.07, which is less than the slope of 0.083, which is required for wheelchairs. $\frac{7}{100} = 0.07$, $\frac{1}{12} = 0.083$
$0.07 < 0.083$ Thus, it is safe.

2.5 Linear Models   pp. 97–104

2.5A Modelling Linear Relationships pp. 97–100

Problem 1

1. a)

Number of Passes, s	Total Pay ($), P
0	20
3	35
6	50
9	65
12	80
15	95
18	110
21	125
24	140
27	155
30	170

b)

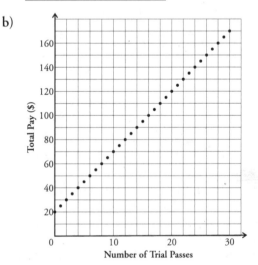

2. a) slope = 5; the slope is the bonus she gets from each trial bass; P-intercept = 20; the P-intercept is her base pay.

3. a) 5   b) $40

4. The graph will be steeper, i.e., has a greater slope; $P = 6s + 20$.
   The P-intercept will be the same.
5. The P-intercept would be 25; $P = 5s + 25$ (parallel).

Part B

$C = 35h + 40$

1. a)

Number of Hours, h	Total Cost ($), C
0	40
1	75
2	110
3	145
4	180
5	215
6	250
7	285
8	320
9	355
10	390

b)

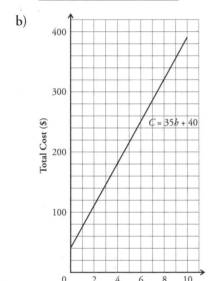

2. slope = 35; the slope is the cost for each hour of work; C-intercept = 40; the C-intercept is the initial cost for a visit
3. a) 3 h   b) $232.50
4. a) The graph would be steeper (greater slope, same C-intercept).
   b) $C = 40h + 40$
5. a) If both companies take the same amount of time for repairs, the other company will charge an extra $10 (parallel).
   b) $C = 35h + 50$

2.5B Modelling Linear Relationships: Pair-Share
pp. 101–104

Problem A

1. a)

Number of Minutes, m	Cost ($), C
0	20
1	20.5
2	21
3	21.5
4	22
5	22.5
6	23
7	23.5
8	24
9	24.5
10	25
11	25.5
12	26
13	26.5
14	27
15	27.5

b)

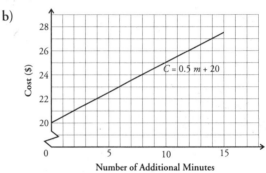

2. slope = 0.5; the slope is the cost of each additional minute; C-intercept = 20; the C-intercept is the initial monthly cost of the phone
3. 8 minutes
4. a) The graph would be steeper (greater slope).
   b) $C = 0.75m + 20$
5. a) If the same amount of time was spent on a cell phone from each company, the cost of the phone from the Listen Up Company would be $10 more (parallel).
   b) $C = 0.5m + 30$

Problem B

$C = 30h + 60$

1. a)

Number of Hours, h	Cost ($), C
0	60
1	90
2	120
3	150
4	180
5	210
6	240
7	270
8	300
9	330
10	360

b)

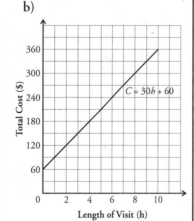

2. slope = 30; the slope is the cost for each hour of work; C-intercept = 60; the C-intercept is the initial cost for a visit
3. 1.5 h
4. a) The graph would be steeper (greater slope).
    b) $C = 40h + 60$
5. a) If both companies take the same amount of time for repairs, the Pipe Works Company will charge $10 less.
    b) $C = 30h + 50$

2.6 The Cartesian Plane   p. 105

Cartesian; René Descartes; x; vertical; origin; coordinates; (x, y) 4

1. H $(-6, 7)$; K $(5, 4)$; M $(-6, -4)$; P $(3, -3)$; Q $(0, -5)$; R $(1, 0)$

2.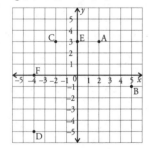

3. Answers will vary.

2.7 The Equation $y = mx + b$ pp. 106–123

2.7A Linear Equations $y = mx + b$ Using Graphing Technology   pp. 106–114

Exercise 1: Linear Equations

linear (or straight lines)

Exercise 2: Non-Linear Equations

non-linear (curves)

a), d), f)

Exercise 3: Parallel Lines and Intercepts

1. b), c)

Equation	Slope	y-intercept
A: $y = 2x + 5$	2	5
B: $y = 2x - 8$	2	−8
C: $y = 2x + 3$	2	3

d) The slopes are equal or the lines are on the same angle. The lines have different y-intercepts.

2. a) $(0, -4)$; 2   b) yes
3. a) $y = 2x + 1$ b) yes
4. b), c)

Equation	Slope	y-intercept
A: $y = -3x + 2$	−3	2
B: $y = -3x + 4$	−3	−4
C: $y = -3x$	−3	0

d) The slopes are equal. The lines have different y-intercepts.

5. a) $(0, 5)$; −3
6. a) $y = -3x + 5$
7. a) slope; y-intercept
    b) m, b c) same slope
    d) i) $y = 4x + 3$ ii) $y = -2x + 7$
       iii) $y = \frac{1}{2}x - 3$

8. a) −3; −4; yes   b) $\frac{3}{5}$; −2; yes   c) $-\frac{1}{2}$; 4; yes

Exercise 4: Perpendicular Lines

1. It is 90°, or perpendicular.
2. It is 90°, or perpendicular.
3. It is 90°, or perpendicular.
4. It is 90°, or perpendicular.
5. a) perpendicular
    b) negative reciprocals
6. a) $3, -\frac{1}{3}$ b) $-\frac{1}{2}, 2$ c) $\frac{17}{11}, -\frac{11}{17}$

Exercise 5

1. 0; They have different slopes.; an infinite number of lines
2. Answers will vary, but must be of the form $y = \_\_x$.
3. Graphs will vary; −2; slope
4. $y = 3x - 7$; $y = -4x - 7$

Exercise 6: More Families, Same Slope

1. Equations and graphs will vary, but must be of the form $y = 3x +$ ___. Yes, they all have the same slope; Yes, the value of b changes in each line.
2. The slope of each line in this family is -2 and each will have different y-intercepts. Second part of answer will vary, but must be of the form $y = -2x +$ ___.
3. $y = 4x - 1$; $y = 4x$

Exercise 7: Horizontal and Vertical Lines

1. a) horizontal line through $y = 4$
    b) horizontal line through $y = -2$
    c) horizontal line through $y = 0$
    d) horizontal line through $y = -5$
    e) $y = b$; 0
2. a) vertical line through $x = 4$
    b) vertical line through $x = -2$
    c) vertical line through $x = 0$
    d) vertical line through $x = -5$
    e) $x = b$; undefined
3. horizontal: a), g); vertical: b), d), h)

2.7B Lines and More Lines   pp. 115–116

1. m, b
2. slope, y-intercept

	Equation	Slope	y-intercept
a)	$y = 2x + 3$	2	3
b)	$y = -2x + 1$	-2	1
c)	$y = \frac{1}{2}x + 4$	$\frac{1}{2}$	4
d)	$y = -3x - 2$	-3	-2

3.

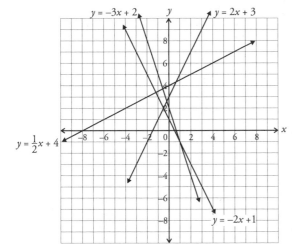

4. A: $b = 2$; point (2, 0); $m = -1$; $y = -x + 2$

   B: $b = 0$; point (1, 2); $m = 2$; $y = 2x$

C: $b = 1$; point (2, –2); $m = -\frac{3}{2}$; $y = -\frac{3}{2} + 1$

D: $b = 2$; point (–3, 0); $m = \frac{2}{3}$; $y = \frac{2}{3} + 2$

5. do not intersect, i.e., the lines are on the same angle; equal
   a) 2
   b) Answers may vary; for example: $y = 2x - 1$; $y = 2x + 3$; $y = 2x + 1$
   c) $-\frac{4}{5}$
   d) Answers may vary; for example: $y = -\frac{4}{5}x$; $y = -\frac{4}{5}x - 1$; $y = -\frac{4}{5}x + 2$

6. have an angle between them of 90°; negative reciprocals
   a) $-\frac{1}{2}$ b) Answers may vary; for example: $y = -\frac{1}{2}x + 4$; $y = -\frac{1}{2}x - 2$; $y = -\frac{1}{2}x$
   c) $\frac{2}{3}$ d) Answers may vary; for example: $y = \frac{2}{3}x + 1$; $y = \frac{2}{3}x + 5$; $y = \frac{2}{3}x - 3$
   e) 4   f) Answers may vary; for example: $y = 4x + 1$; $y = 4x - 4$; $y = 4x$

2.7C Equations of Lines: Chart   p. 117

1.

Equation	Slope	y-intercept	Slope of Line Parallel to This Line	Slope of Line Perpendicular to This Line
1. $y = 5x + 1$	5	1	5	$-\frac{1}{5}$
2. $y = -2x - 7$	-2	-7	-2	$\frac{1}{2}$
3. $y = \frac{3}{5}x + 2$	$\frac{3}{5}$	2	$\frac{3}{5}$	$-\frac{5}{3}$
4. $y = 2x + 7$	2	7	2	$-\frac{1}{2}$
5. $y = -4x + 8$	-4	8	-4	$\frac{1}{4}$
6. $y = -4x + 3$	-4	3	-4	$\frac{1}{4}$
7. $y = \frac{1}{2}x + 5$	$\frac{1}{2}$	5	$\frac{1}{2}$	-2
8. $y = \frac{2}{3}x$	$\frac{2}{3}$	0	$\frac{2}{3}$	$-\frac{3}{2}$
9. $y = x$	1	0	1	-1
10. $y = 7$	0	7	0	undefined
11. $x = 2$	undefined	none	undefined	0

2. Answers may vary. For Example, A: $y = -\frac{2}{5}x + 2$; B: $y = \frac{3}{2}x + 4$; C: $y = 1.5x - 2$

2.7D Find the Equation of a Line   pp. 118

1.

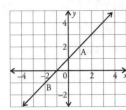

$m = 1$
$b = 1$
$y = x + 1$

2.

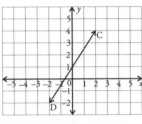

$m = \dfrac{2}{3}$

$b = 1$

$y = \dfrac{3}{2}x + 1$

3.

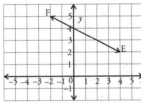

$m = -\dfrac{1}{2}$

$b = 4$

$y = -\dfrac{1}{2}x + 4$

4.

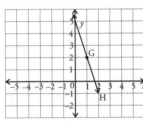

$m = -3$
$b = 5$
$y = -3x + 5$

2.7E Find the Equation of the Line That Represents the Cost   pp. 119–120

1. (5, 350), (8, 500)

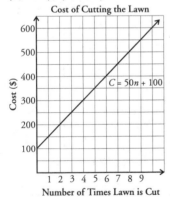

Cost of Cutting the Lawn

Rate: $50/cut
Initial cost: $100
$C = 50n + 100$

2. (50, 450), (30, 300)

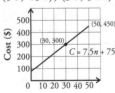

Rate: $7.50/person
Initial cost: $75
$C = 7.5n + 75$

3. (3, 6.5), (6, 11)

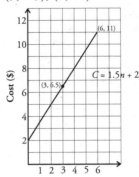

Rate: $1.50/km
Initial cost: $2
$C = 1.5n + 2$

4. (30, 110), (90, 230)

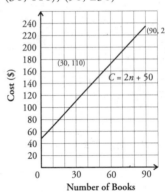

Rate: $2/book
Initial cost: $50
$C = 2n + 50$

2.7F Graphing Lines: Three Methods
pp. 121–122

Example 1

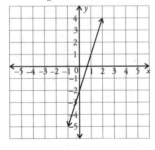

Method 1

x	y
−1	−5
0	−2
1	1
2	4

Method 2
$b = -2;\ m = 3$

Example 2

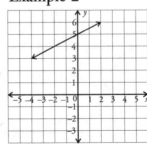

Method 1

x	y
−4	3
−2	4
0	5
2	6

Method 2
$b = 5;\ m = \dfrac{1}{2}$

Example 3

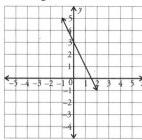

Method 1

x	y
−1	5
0	3
1	1
2	−1

Method 2
$b = 3; \; m = -2$

Example 4

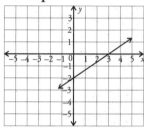

Method 3

x	y
0	−2
3	0

x-intercept = 3;
y-intercept = −2

Example 5

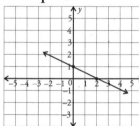

Method 3

x	y
0	1
2	0

x-intercept = 2;
y-intercept = 1

If the equations are of the form $y = mx + b$, Method 2 is usually easiest.

If the equations are of the form $ax + by = c$, Method 3 is easiest.

2.8 Linear Models for Comparison Shopping
pp. 123–126

2.8A Example of Comparison Shopping
pp. 123–124

a) A: $C = 200 + 15h$; B: $C = 250 + 10h$; C: $C = 25h$

b)

c) A: never; B: for more than 16 h 40 min, approximately 17 h; C: for less than 16 h 40 min, approximately 17 h.

2.8B Comparison Shopping: Practice
pp. 125–126

1.

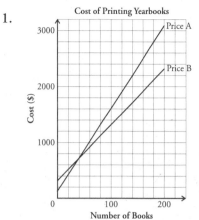

A: $C = 100 + 15n$; B: $C = 300 + 10n$
The deals are equal for 40 books.
Price A is better for up to 40 books.
Price B is better for more than 40 books.

2.

A: $C = 20 + 5n$; B: $C = 15 + 8n$
Price A is better for more than 1 T-shirt.
Price B is better for only 1 T-shirt.

3.

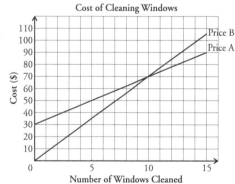

A: $C = 30 + 4n$; B: $C = 7n$
Both prices are the same for 10 windows.
Price A is better for more than 10 windows.
Price B is better for less than 10 windows.

4.

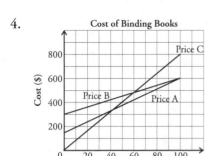

Cost of Binding Books

A: $C = 150 + 4.5n$; B: $C = 300 + 3n$; C: $C = 8n$

Price C is best for up to 40 books.

Price A is best for between 40 to 100 books.

Prices A and C are the same for 40 books.

Price B is never the best price.

5.

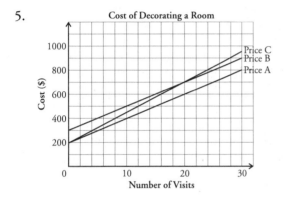

Cost of Decorating a Room

A: $C = 200 + 20n$; B: $C = 300 + 20n$;

C: $C = 200 + 25n$

Price A is always the best price.

Teacher's Resource Answers

Unit 2   Algebra and Relations

A2.1B Exponents: Quiz   pp. 67–68

1. a) $(3)(3)(3)(3)(3)$ b) $(-1)(-1)(-1)$
2. a) 2^6 b) $(-40)^4$ c) $(3)^3(1.7)^4$
3. 5: exponent; 7: base; : 7^5 power
4. a) 3^{23} b) 5^7 c) 4^6
   d) $(2)^{11}(3)^9$ e) 3^7
5. a) 2^6 b) 10^5
6. $3 \times 4 = 3 + 3 + 3 + 3$ and $3^4 = 3 \times 3 \times 3 \times 3$
7. $\dfrac{4 \times 4 \times 4 \times 4 \times 4 \times 4 \times 4}{4 \times 4 \times 4} = 4 \times 4 \times 4 \times 4 = 4^4$
8. $(-3)^2 = (-3)(-3)$; $-3^2 = -3 \times 3$

A2.2 Scientific Notation and Exponents: Quiz   p. 69

1. a) 3^8 b) 2^7 c) $\dfrac{1}{5^8}$
   d) x^8 e) $6y^7$
2. a) The base is negative.
   b) The exponent is negative. It means $\dfrac{1}{4^3}$.
3. a) 231 000 000   b) 0.000 000 023 1
4. a) 2.5×10^9 b) 7.51×10^{-6}
5. a) 6.6×10^{24} b) 1.5×10^{-15}
6. 9×10^{-18} g

A2.4B Slope: Quiz   pp. 70–71

1. a) $\dfrac{1}{3}$ b) $\dfrac{3}{2}$
2. a) $\dfrac{6}{7}$ b) $\dfrac{-1}{2}$
3. $\dfrac{1}{5}$
4. Possibility 1: rise 2, run 3; possibility 2: rise –2, run –3.
5. a) Both lines are equally as steep.
   b) The line with the positive slope rises from left to right. The line with the negative slope falls from left to right.
6. a) $\dfrac{2}{24} = \dfrac{1}{12}$ (safe)   b) $\dfrac{0.5}{4.5} > \dfrac{1}{12}$ (not safe)
7. A 0; B $\dfrac{1}{4}$; C –1; D –4; E 4; F $-\dfrac{1}{4}$; G 1
8. The greater the slope is, the steeper the hill is. Since $\dfrac{8}{5}$ is greater than $\dfrac{5}{8}$, she will choose the hill with slope $\dfrac{8}{5}$.

A2.5B Modelling Linear Relationships: Quiz

pp. 72–73

1.

d ($)	C ($)
1	225
2	250
3	275
4	300
5	325
6	350
7	375
8	400
9	425
10	450

2.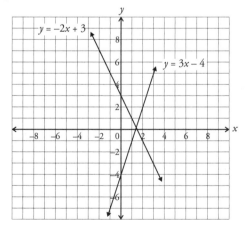

3. a) slope = 25; *C*-intercept = 200
   b) The slope is the daily rental charge. The *C*-intercept is the fixed cost for the guide.

4. 3 days

5. a) The graph would be steeper.
   b) $C = 30d + 200$

6. a) The Trail Company trips are always more expensive than the Canoe Company trips by $100 (parallel).
   b) $C = 25d + 300$

A2.6 The Cartesian Plane: Assignment

p. 74

Answers may vary.

A2.7B Slopes and Lines: Quiz

p. 75

1. a) Lines A and D are parallel.
   b) Lines C and F are perpendicular.
   c) Lines A and E cross at the same point on the *y*-axis.

2. a), b)

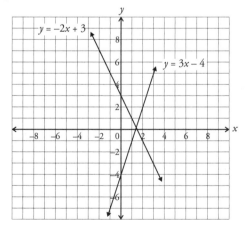

3. B, D, and F are non-linear.

A2.7C Linear Equations

p. 76

Line 1: $y = 5$; Line 2: $x = -5$;

Line 3: $y = x - 2$; Line 4: $y = -\frac{1}{2}x + 1$

A2.7D Lines and More Lines: Quiz

pp. 77-78

1. slope, *y*-intercept
2. a) 3, 1   b) −2, −5   c) $y = -2x - 3$
3.

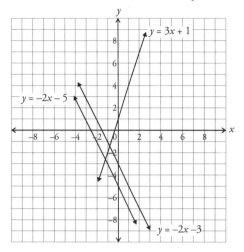

4. Slope of line A = $\frac{2}{3}$, slope of line B = $-\frac{3}{2}$, slope of line C = $-\frac{3}{2}$. Lines A and B are perpendicular since the product of their slopes is −1. Lines B and C are parallel since their slopes are the same.

5. $y = -\frac{2}{3}x$

6. a) $\frac{1}{2}$ b) Answers may vary.

7. a) $\frac{1}{3}$ b), c) Answers may vary. For example,

$$y = \frac{1}{3}x + 2 \text{ or } y = \frac{1}{3}x - 1$$

2.8B Comparison Shopping: Quiz

p. 79

1. Answers may vary.
2. Lawns R Us: $C = 30h + 240$
   Clean and Green: $C = 60h$
3. Answers may vary. For example,

Lawns R Us		Clean and Green	
Number of Hours	Total Cost ($)	Number of Hours	Total Cost ($)
4	360	4	240
8	480	8	480
12	600	12	720
16	720	16	960
20	840	20	1200

4. Lawns R Us is cheaper for jobs longer than 8 h. Clean and Green is cheaper for jobs shorter than 8 h. The jobs cost the same for 8 h.
5. reliability, environmental safety, and quality of work

Review Part 1: Finding Slopes

p. 80

1. a) $\frac{25}{125} > \frac{1}{10}$ (not safe)   b) $\frac{18}{200} < \frac{1}{10}$ (safe)

2. a) slope $= \frac{3}{7}$ b) slope $= \frac{-7}{5}$

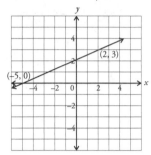
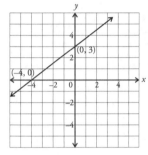

c) slope $= \frac{3}{4}$

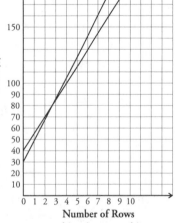

3. a), b) Answers may vary.

c) Line A: $\frac{2}{3}$, Line B: 3, Line C: $\frac{1}{3}$

Review Part 2: Find the Cost

pp. 81–82

1. a) $C = 15r + 40$ b) $100

2. a) $C = 5b + 1000$ b) $2500

3. a) $C = 0.10n + 5$ b) $1005

4. a)

r	$C(\$)$
1	55
2	70
3	85
4	100
5	115
6	130
7	145
8	160

b)

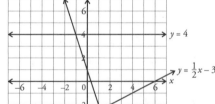

c) 15

d) The slope is the cost per room.

e) 40

f) The C-intercept is the fixed cost for supplies.

5. a) $C = 19r + 30$ b) (on graph)

c) Line $C = 15r + 40$ is not as steep as line $C = 19r + 30$, because the slope (cost per room) is less. Line $C = 15r + 40$ is positioned higher up on the Cost axis, because the cost of supplies is more that the cost of supplies in line $C = 19r + 30$.

d) For fewer than three rooms the second company, $C = 19r + 30$, charges less. If you are cleaning three or more rooms, the first company, $C = 15r + 40$, will charge you less.

Review Part 3: Lines

p. 83

A: $y = -3x - 5$; B: $y = -2x + 4$;

C: $y = \frac{1}{2}x + 2$; D: $y = \frac{1}{2}x$

2. a) Lines C and D are parallel, since their slopes are the same.

b) Lines C and D are perpendicular to line B, since their slopes are negative reciprocals,

i.e., $-2 \times \frac{1}{2} = -1$

3. a), b), c)

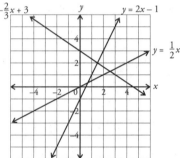

4. various answers with

a) slope $\frac{2}{3}$ b) slope $\frac{-1}{2}$ c) y-intercept 0

Review Part 4: Algebra

pp. 84–85

1. a) $8x + 3$ b) $-3y - 3x$ c) $6m + 3k$
   d) $16m - 6$ e) $22z + 12$ f) $2x^2 + s$ g) -3

2. a) $\frac{25}{3}$ b) 3   c) $-\frac{19}{6}$ d) $\frac{15}{7}$

   e) 7.5   f) L.S.= 23; R.S. = 23

3.

4. a) A: $y = 2x + 3$;
        B: $x = 6$
    b) $y = -3x$

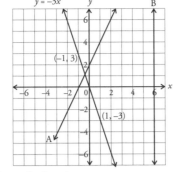

5. a)

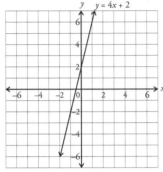

    b) various answers with $m = 4$
    c), e), g) Answers may vary.
    d) various answers with $m = \dfrac{-1}{4}$
    f) various answers with $b = 2$

Review Part 5: Exponents   p. 86

1. a) 3^{12} b) 7^{10} c) 4^{13} d) 2^{15}
    e) 6^{16} f) 5^{13} g) $2^7 3^4$ h) 2^3
2. a) 3 b) 7^2 c) 4 d) 8^{11}
    e) 2 f) 1 g) 6^9 h) $\dfrac{2^5}{3^4}$
3. a) 2^{15} b) 3^{12} c) $3^{16}5^{15}$ d) 2^{18}
4. a) x^{10} b) x^3 c) y^{11} d) j^2
    e) c^7 f) z^2s^8 g) m^{10} h) q^{16}

Final Assessment Introduction: Relations and Algebra

Part 1: Let's Rent a Car   pp. 88–89

1.

Plan 1		Plan 2		Plan 3	
d	C ($)	d	C ($)	d	C ($)
2	60	2	90	2	200
4	120	4	130	4	200
6	180	6	170	6	200
8	240	8	210	8	200
10	300	10	250	10	200
12	360	12	290	12	200
14	420	14	330	14	200
16	480	16	370	16	400
18	540	18	410	18	400
20	600	20	450	20	400

2.

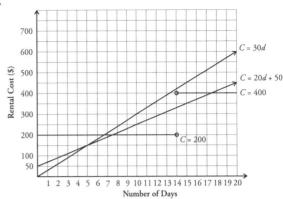

3. Rental Plan 1: $C = 30d$
    Rental Plan 2: $C = 20d + 50$

Conclusions

1. Plan 1 is least expensive for $120.
2. Plan 2 is least expensive for $190.
3. Plan 3 is least expensive for $200
4. Use Plan 1 for trips up to, and including, 5 days. Use Plan 2 for trips 6 or 7 days long and Plan 3 for trips of 8 or more days.
5. For $450 he could get 28 days from Plan 3, 20 days from Plan 2, and 15 days from Plan 1.
6. He should consider insurance coverage and the type and size of the car.

Part 2: How Much Gas Is Needed?   pp. 90–92

1. Answers may vary.
2.

Distance Travelled (km)	Fuel Gauge Reading
0	1
200	0.875
270	0.75
350	0.625
400	0.5
440	0.375
470	0.25
485	0.125
500	0

3.

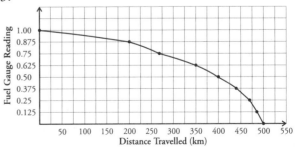

4. Answers may vary
5. No. It shows that the car consumes gas at a faster rate as the tank empties.

6. 0.4 of the tank is remaining.
7. On the graph, 0.6 full is approximately 360 km.
8. Answers may vary.
9. a) 10 tanks of gas   b) Answers may vary.
10. Answers may vary.

Part 3: Storing Your Antique Car   pp. 93–94

1.

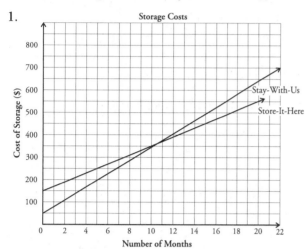

2. Store-It-Here: $C = 20m + 150$
   Stay-With-Us: $C = 30m + 50$
3. Answers may vary.
4.

Company	Cost for 6 Months in a Year ($)	Cost for 10 Months in a Year ($)
Store-It-Here	270	350
Stay-With-Us	230	350

5. After 10 months, Store-It-Here is always cheaper.
6. He needs to consider the location, size, and security of the storage area.

Part 4: Other Possibilities   pp. 95–97

1. linear; daily rate is constant positive;
   costs are increasing
   Yes; they all have the same daily rate.
   No; they are parallel.
   Choose Plan A, since it is always cheaper than the other two plans.
2. linear; daily rate is constant positive;
   costs are increasing
   No; daily rates are different.
   Yes; they intersect at the C-intercept, which is the cost for insurance.
3. non-linear; losing energy at different rates
   negative; amount of power left is decreasing
   Answers may vary.

4. linear; walking rate is constant
   positive; distance from home is increasing
   negative; distance from work is decreasing as time is increasing
5. a), b) Answers may vary.

Unit 2 Final Final Assessment   pp. 98–100

1. a) $-x + 8$ b) $24a - 11b$
2. $-2x + 5y$; -16

3. a) $\frac{1}{5^2} = \frac{1}{25}$ b) $\frac{2^3}{3^3} = \frac{8}{27}$ c) $2^2 = 4$
   d) $(5^3)(4^5)$ e) x^9 f) $-24y^{11}$
4. a) 3   b) -6
   c) 1   d) L.S. = -25; R.S. = -25
5.

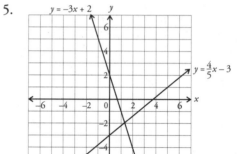

6. a) A: $y = \frac{2}{3}x + 2$; B: $y = -3x - 4$
   b) $y = 2x - 5$

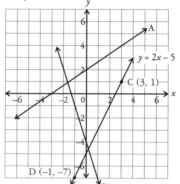

7. a) various answers with $m = 5$
   b) various answers with $m = -\frac{1}{5}$
   c) various answers with $b = -7$
8. No. $\frac{32}{360} > \frac{1}{12}$
9. a) 0.000 004 2   b) 8.91×10^8
   c) 8.4×10^2
10. 9.48×10^{15} m

Unit 3 Teaching Notes

Section 3.1 Area and Perimeter

Sections 3.6 and 3.7 use *The Geometer's Sketchpad®* software. If computers are limited, Sections 3.1 to 3.5 can be done in conjunction with Sections 3.6 and 3.7, so the students can share the available computers.

3.1A Rectangles

3.1B Area and Perimeter: Class Activity

3.1C Area and Perimeter: Combined Shapes

Student Resource pp. 130–132

Teaching Suggestions

Display the activity pages on an overhead projector for easy instruction and review of the answers. Some students may be much better at this than others. Do not overemphasize the formula approach for area. There is really only one formula at this point, $A = bh$, with variations of this formula. The students can complete the activities in rotation, doing Activity 3.1B while working on Activities 3.1A and 3.1C, so not all students are moving around the room at the same time. The students may find it helpful if you break up combined shapes into their basic geometric shapes, shade the different geometric shapes with colours, and do the calculation for that shape in that colour. Encourage the students to do this as well.

Common Errors

- Students need reinforcement that the height of a triangle is perpendicular height.
- Some students will continue to need reinforcement of the difference between perimeter and area.

3.1D Area and Perimeter: Applications

Student Resource pp. 133–135

Teaching Suggestions

Lead a discussion about why finding area or perimeter might be important to them. The ideas in question 1 are repeated in questions 2 and 3, so the teacher could lead or instruct the students through question 1 and, then, have the students do questions 2 and 3 independently. The shaded margins can be used for formulas, converting percents to decimals, etc.

In Question 4, the students need to divide the hexagon into 6 congruent triangles.

Common Errors

Some review for questions 1b) and 1c) may be needed before completing this activity.

Specific Expectations
NA3.05, MG2.01, MG2.03

Overall Goals and Key Concepts
- recall and use formulas for area and perimeter of rectangles and triangles

Materials
- overhead projector

Timing
75 min

Related Resources
MATHPOWER™ 9, Ontario Edition, Blackline Masters
Masters 9.1 (Choose appropriate questions.)

Specific Expectations
NA3.05, MG2.01, MG2.03, MG2.04

Overall Goals and Key Concepts
- use area and perimeter in a real life application

Timing
75 min

Related Resources
MATHPOWER™ 9, Ontario Edition, Blackline Masters
Master 2.8 (percent)

Specific Expectations
MG2.01, MG2.03

Overall Goals and Key
Concepts
- apply area and perimeter
  to real life problems and
  tie in problem solving

Materials
- *Assessment Master 26,*
  A3.1E Area and Perimeter

Timing
15 min to review
expectations

Related Resources
MATHPOWER™ 9,
Ontario Edition,
Blackline Masters
pages 68–70 "An Interior
Design Project"

3.1E Area Assignment: Redecorate a Room

Student Resource p. 136

Teaching Suggestions

Make your expectations for this assignment clear, including due date. Suggest that the students find out the price of paint, wallpaper, and floor covering to make the activity as realistic as possible. Some students may want to use additional pages to write the complete solutions. Some students may choose to get paint chips and carpet samples to reach a level 4 answer.

Common Errors

You may need to revisit scale drawings with some of the students.

Assessment

Distribute *Assessment Master 26,* A3.1E Area and Perimeter, and have the students complete it. Collect and mark it for formative assessment.

Section 3.2 Maximum Areas

3.2A A Swimmingly Great Problem

Student Resource pp. 137–140

Teaching Suggestions

Demonstrate, using grid paper on an overhead projector, how the area of a rectangle changes as the dimensions change, even with a fixed perimeter. Guide students through questions 1–4 with the students working along and taking some leadership. It is not necessary to include every possible value for length and width. It is also worth noting how the values in the table become reversed, (i.e., length of 29 and width of 1 at the beginning of the chart, length of 1 and width of 29 at the end of the chart). Discuss the correct labelling and scaling for the graph.

Discuss this interesting line of best fit (parabola) and what it is telling them in terms of maximum area. Have students complete questions 6–8 on their own and then check their answers with a classmate.

Specific Expectations
NA3.05, NA4.01, NA4.02,
NA4.03, MG1.01, MG1.04,
G2.03, MG2.04

Overall Goals and Key
Concepts
- explore what happens to
  the area of a rectangle
  with a constant perimeter
  as the dimensions vary

Materials
- overhead projector
- large grid paper

Timing
75 min

"Be tough about the behaviour, but be caring and supportive of the person."
Harvey Silver and Bart Mindszenthy

Specific Expectations

NA3.05, NA4.01, NA4.02, NA4.03, MG1.01, MG1.04, G2.03, MG2.04

Overall Goals and Key Concepts

- explore what happens to the area of a rectangle with a constant perimeter as the dimensions vary

Materials

- overhead projector
- large grid paper

Timing

75 min

3.2B Down the Garden Path: Maximum Area

Student Resource pp. 141–142

Teaching Suggestions

Explain to students that the problem in this activity is similar to the one in the previous activity (swimming area problem). Working in pairs might be helpful in this exercise, but the ultimate goal is for students to do this independently. Encourage the students to draw diagrams.

Common Errors

Check that students label the axis properly and choose an appropriate scale.

Section 3.3 Circles

3.3A Pi Development

Student Resource pp. 143–144

Teaching Suggestions

Gather round flat objects, of varying sizes, and measuring tapes (or string and ruler) for each pair or group of students. Go through the instructions with students by showing them how to measure the circumference and diameter accurately. Fill out the first row of the chart with this data. Have groups choose round objects and measure them until their data are collected. Have the students finish the activity independently.

Point out that this activity developed the formula for the perimeter (circumference) of a circle. The area formula can be given to them, or developed using other techniques found in most math texts. This activity allows a timely review and demonstrates an application of linear equations.

A historical discussion of pi (Euler's name) may be of interest.

Common Errors

Check that students use an appropriate scale and label the axes properly. Some students may have difficulty identifying the slope as approximately 3.14 or pi. This can be discussed when you take up the conclusions with the class.

Specific Expectations

NA4.01, NA4.02, NA4.03, AG1.03 RE1.04, RE1.05 AG2.01, AG2.02, AG2.03, AG2.04, AG3.01, AG3.02, AG3.04, AG3.05

Overall Goals and Key Concepts

- develop the formula for the circumference of a circle
- review hypothesis, data collection, scatter plots, and finding the equation of the line of best fit

Materials

- round flat objects of various sizes
- measuring tapes
- string
- rulers

Timing

45 min

"Being fair does not mean treating every student the same."

T. Anne and Rod Yeager

Specific Expectations
NA2.02, NA3.05, MG2.01, MG2.03

Overall Goals and Key Concepts
- use formulas to find the area and the perimeter of a circle
- solve problems involving the area and the perimeter of a circle, and of figures that are a combination of other shapes and circles

Materials
- overhead projector

Timing
75 min

Related Resources
MATHPOWER™ 9, Ontario Edition, Blackline Masters
Master 9.1 (Select)

3.3B Circle: Area and Circumference

Student Resource pp. 145–147

Teaching Suggestions

Using an overhead projector, have the students model solutions for examples 1 and 2 and for part circles. Discuss leaving the answer in terms of π or replacing π with 3.14 under certain conditions.

Some students may need more practice finding area and perimeter of circles and part circles before moving on to the problem solving and combination area and perimeter questions 2 to 6.

Common Errors

- Students sometimes forget to take half the diameter for the radius. Remind the students that r^2 means $(r)(r)$, not $2r$.
- When finding the perimeter of a partial circle, students often forget to include the straight side(s).

Assessment

Distribute *Assessment Master 28*, A3.3B Circles, and have the students complete it. Collect and mark it for formative assessment.

"Success: ninety nine percent perspiration, one percent inspiration."

Anonymous

Specific Expectations
NA2.01, NA2.03, NA3.05

Overall Goals and Key Concepts
- review areas of circles and triangles, with communication

Materials
- *Assessment Master 28*, A3.3C Area and Perimeter

Timing
20 min

Related Resources
MATHPOWER™ 9, Ontario Edition, Blackline Masters
Master 9.1 (Select)

3.3C Areas of Combined Shapes

Student Resource p. 148

Teaching Suggestions

Circulate to be sure students are sharing the writing and the talking. Remember that pair-share means one pencil and one paper for each pair. When completed, each student can do the other question independently or for homework. More practice is recommended.

Common Errors

Some students may need to review the area of triangles.

Assessment

Distribute *Assessment Master 28*, A3.3C Area and Perimeter, and have the students complete it. Collect and mark it for formative assessment.

Specific Expectations
NA3.05, MG2.01, MG2.03

Overall Goals and Key
Concepts
- solve a problem about
  circles

Timing
20 min

3.3D Round and Round and Round

Student Resource p. 149

Teaching Suggestions

Set the stage for this activity by discussing the question and having the students discuss it, and then guess their answer. Let them work on the problem in pairs for about 10 minutes to come up with an equation (or other method) to solve it. Circulate and suggest approaches, if necessary. Have the students explain their thinking to you. If the students are continuing to work through this problem on their own, let them continue. Otherwise, regroup the class and ask for ideas. Finish the activity as a class. (Alternatively, it could be an assignment to be considered the next day.)

Section 3.4 Pythagorean Theorem

3.4A Pythagorean Theorem Puzzle

Student Resource p. 150

Specific Expectations
NA3.04

Overall Goals and Key
Concepts
- understand the
  Pythagorean theorem by
  seeing it in a concrete
  format

Materials
- *Teacher Resource Master
  14* (Pythagorean Theorem
  Puzzle)
- glue sticks
- scissors

Timing
20 min

Teaching Suggestions

Glue sticks and scissors are needed, and copies of the Pythagorean Theorem Puzzle from the *Teacher Resource Master 14*. Find out some interesting information about Pythagoras and tell a story about him (or have some students do this). Define a right triangle and the hypotenuse and the two sides. Point out that the puzzle is constructed by drawing squares on the sides and on the hypotenuse of the right triangle. Have each student cut and paste his or her puzzle onto the student resource page and make a conclusion. This activity is designed to compare the areas of the squares on the sides of a right triangle. Have the students highlight the Pythagorean theorem on the student resource page. Stress the importance of knowing which side is the hypotenuse.

It may be worth noting that it does not have to be the areas of squares; many regular shapes will work, such as semicircles, equilateral triangles, or hexagons. This would be an excellent extension activity.

Be sure the students cut the pieces labelled 1, 2, 3, 4, and 5. They then glue to their student resource page the right triangle with the square on the hypotenuse still attached. Have the students arrange pieces 1 to 5 to fit exactly in the square on the hypotenuse.

"It is the teacher's job to teach the way a student learns, not the student's job to learn the way a teacher teaches.

T. Anne and Rod Yeager

Specific Expectations
NA3.04, NA3.05

Overall Goals and Key Concepts
- Apply the Pythagorean theorem to find any side of a right triangle

Materials
- overhead projector

Timing
50 min

Related Resources
MATHPOWER™ 9, Ontario Edition, Blackline Masters
Masters 3.12 (Omit the formulas for 35. Just do the questions.), 7.8 (questions 9 and 10)

3.4B Using the Pythagorean Theorem

Student Resource pp. 151–152

Warm Up
Explain what is meant by a radical (square root) sign. Have the students find this key on their calculators and do a few problems using it (i.e., find the square root of 25, 144, 70, 105, etc.). They could approximate/guess, and then check using a calculator.

Teaching Suggestions
Do examples 1 to 4 with the students on an overhead transparency, to show the proper form. Gradually let them do some steps on their own, taking them up as you go. More practice may be needed. This provides more practice in solving equations.

Common Errors
- When using the Pythagorean theorem to find the missing side, suggest that the students start with the basic formula and rearrange after substitution if necessary.
- Remind the students that a^2 means $(a)(a)$, not $2a$. Use the radical sign and discuss when the students should leave the answer in radical form and when they should approximate the answer.

Specific Expectations
NA3.04, NA3.05

Overall Goals and Key Concepts
- communicate and use the Pythagorean theorem

Materials
- *Assessment Master 29*, A3.4C Pythagorean Theorem

Timing
20 min

3.4C More Pythagoras

Student Resource p. 153

Teaching Suggestions
Circulate to be sure students are using the correct formula and format for solving. Watch that students also find the area of the first triangle. Listen for good mathematical language when discussing the second question, and check that students also write the answer and show a diagram to help explain. Be sure that the students are sharing the writing and the explaining of the theorem.

Assessment
Distribute *Assessment Master 29*, A3.4C Pythagorean Theorem, and have the students complete it. Collect and mark it for formative assessment.

Section 3.5 Three-Dimensional Geometry

Specific Expectations
MG2.02, MG2.03

Overall Goals and Key Concepts
- visualize three-dimensional figures and their corresponding nets

3.5A Nets and Solids

Student Resource p. 154

Teaching Suggestions
Bring in nets that can be formed into three-dimensional solids, or provide the students with these nets to cut and build solids. Nets are available in many resources. Alternatively, ask the students to bring in a box (of an interesting shape, if possible) that can be cut into its net. Discuss the names of the solids,

Materials
- nets of three-dimensional solids

Timing
30–60 min

Specific Expectations
NA3.05, MG2.02, MG2.03

Overall Goals and Key Concepts
- find the surface area of three-dimensional solids by using nets
- divide nets into shapes (rectangles, triangles, circles)
- use the proper form of the solution

Materials
- nets of three-dimensional solids
- *Teacher Resource Master 15*, Three-Dimensional Geometry Solids
- *Assessment Master 30*, A3.5B Paint the Walls

Timing
200 min

Related Resources
MATHPOWER™ 9, Ontario Edition, Blackline Masters
Masters 9.2, 9.3, 9.4 (Select surface area questions from pages 38-47.)

pointing out the difference between prisms and pyramids. This difference is particularly important when developing formulas for volume. To visualize prisms, use analogies, such as, a loaf of bread in which all slices are the same, or an elevator shaft. Have these nets available throughout this section for demonstration purposes, and for the students to use when necessary.

The nets of any solids from Column 2 that are not matched could be drawn in the shaded margin of the student resource page. Each solid could be named.

3.5B Surface Area of Prisms

3.5C Three-Dimensional Geometry: Surface Area

Student Resource pp. 155–157

Teaching Suggestions

In question 1 of Activity 3.5B, have the net of a triangular prism available to show how the shape folds and unfolds into the picture on the student resource page. There are many real-life models, such as a Toblerone box, that can be collected for classroom use, and cut up to show the net. For the Toblerone box, show the solution as the sum of the areas of two triangles and three rectangles. Use the formulas for the area of a triangle and of a rectangle. Suggest that the student write the formula in the shaded margin of the student resource book.

In question 2 of Activity 3.5B, have on hand a net of a cylinder to show that the surface area consists of one rectangle and two circles. Cut-up frozen juice cans work well. Have all the dimensions put on the net. In this question, only one circle (the top) of the silo is included in the total surface area.

In Activity 3.5C, the chart helps the students organize the solution. In the shaded border, students can place formulas for rectangles, circles, and triangles for quick reference for the areas of shapes. The intent of the chart is to emphasize that each net is made up of a combination of basic shapes. Have nets available to students. Provide the students with *Teacher Resource Master 15* of this chart for further problems, practice, or assessment.

Common Errors
- In the first example of Activity 3.5C, explain that sometimes the rectangles are not the same size and must then be done separately. Have a net to demonstrate this.
- In the second example of Activity 3.5C, show that the length of the rectangle fits around the circular base, and therefore its length is the circumference of the circle. Many students find this difficult to remember.
- Check that the students put the dimensions on the nets, and that they do not assume that all the rectangles are the same size.

Assessment
Distribute *Assessment Master 30*, A3.5B Paint the Walls, and have the students complete it. Collect and mark it for formative assessment.

Specific Expectations

NA3.05, MG2.02, MG2.03

Overall Goals and Key Concepts

- learn and apply the formula for the volume of a prism

Materials

- 10 equal-sized congruent rectangles, triangles, and circles

Timing

45 min plus practice time

Related Resources

MATHPOWER™ 9, Ontario Edition, Blackline Masters Masters 9.2, 9.3, 9.4 (Select questions involving the volume of prisms.)

3.5D Volume of a Prism

Student Resource p. 158

Teaching Suggestions

Using the 10 equal-sized congruent rectangles, demonstrate how, when stacked, these rectangles make prisms of different heights and therefore different volumes. The analogies given in Activity 3.5A of this teacher's resource (bread and elevator) continue to work well. Explain to the students that the size of the base was the same — just the height changed; therefore, the volume can be expressed as (area of the base)(height). Do the same with triangular and circular shapes.

Generalize the formula for the volume of all prisms as Bh where B represents the area of the base. Do this by picturing prisms as a loaf of bread or an elevator shaft again. Do examples 1 and 2 to demonstrate the formula and the proper form through to the solution. More practice is required.

Common Errors

- Explain to the students how they could figure out which side is the base.

> "When communicating with the home, layer your concerns with positive statements."
>
> T. Anne and Rod Yeager

3.5E Volume of a Pyramid

Student Resource p. 159

Teaching Suggestions

Explain the difference between a prism and a pyramid. Have hollow three-dimensional prisms and pyramids with congruent bases and common heights, and pourable materials with which to fill them. (Rice, oatmeal, water, and confetti all work.)

Demonstrate to the students what they will be doing as they proceed to the different stations where corresponding figures are placed. Emphasize the need for accuracy when measuring. Each group should have the opportunity to complete the activity with more than one substance, and then develop a formula for the relationship between the volumes of a prism and a pyramid after doing the activity.

Discuss the formula for the volume of a pyramid, showing that it is not really new, just an adjustment upon the formula for the volume of a prism (i.e., divide by 3). Do some examples and provide additional practice.

Assessment

Distribute *Assessment Master 31*, A3.5E Area and Volume, and have the students complete it. Collect and mark it for formative assessment.

> "In the psychological realm of relationship between teacher and child, the teacher's part and its techniques are analogous to those of the valet: they are to serve, and to serve well: to serve the spirit."
>
> Dr. Maria Montessori

Specific Expectations

NA3.05, MG2.02, MG2.03, MG2.05

Overall Goals and Key Concepts

- learn and apply the formula for the volume of a pyramid

Materials

- hollow three-dimensional prisms and pyramids
- pourable materials such as rice, oatmeal, water, and confetti
- *Assessment Master 31*, A3.5E Area and Volume

Timing

45 min

Related Resources

MATHPOWER™ 9, Ontario Edition, Blackline Masters Masters 9.2, 9.3, 9.4 (Select questions involving the volume of pyramids.)

Specific Expectations

NA3.03, NA4.01, NA4.02, NA4.03, MG1.02, MG1.04

Overall Goals and Key Concepts

- find the minimum surface area of a prism of fixed volume
- review scatter plots and data collection

Materials

- 1-cm interlocking cubes

Timing

75 min

Related Resources

MATHPOWER™ 9, Ontario Edition, Blackline Masters pages 48–53 (Building a Better Box)

3.5F Minimum Surface Area: Rectangular Prism

Student Resource pp. 160–162

Warm Up

Introduce this activity by leading a class discussion on when, in real life, it might be necessary to find the surface area of a given volume, and, in particular, why the minimum surface area might be important.

Teaching Suggestions

Provide each group with 64 1-cm interlocking cubes. Give the students 15 minutes for creative play with the cubes. For example, ask them to make any solid that uses all their cubes, or share the cubes among the students in the group and ask each student to make a solid, or solid letters that spell the word "math." At this point, have each group complete the activity on its own, or work through the activity with the class in the following way. Have each group of students build a rectangular prism that uses all the cubes. Ask the groups to work out the area of the base, the height, the entire surface area, and the volume of the solid and put their results on the chart given on student resource page 160. Note that any rectangular prism could have three different bases depending on the orientation. Have each group show its solid to the class and describe how it found the surface area and volume. If you need more data, ask groups to make specific solids as required and put data on the chart. When the data have been collected, have the students draw a scatter plot and graph.

The scatter plot will produce several curves, but remind the students that they are looking for the minimum value. Check the graphs and the conclusions. Complete the activity individually, in groups, or as a class. There are seven different prisms with 16 different bases. The chart has been predetermined. Specific bases have been placed in the chart to optimize the students' efficiency. Students may discover that all cases are not present in the chart. Questions 4 to 8 will solidify the conclusions drawn from this activity and Activity 3.2B Down the Garden Path: Maximum Area. Discussion of solutions will be necessary.

Common Errors

When the students are creating the scatter plot, check that they plot the area of the base along the horizontal axis and the surface area along the vertical axis.

"You can learn many things from children. How much patience you have, for example."

Franklin P. Jones

Overall Goals and Key Concepts

- recognize that a cylinder with a particular surface area can represent cylinders of different volumes

Materials

- sheets of paper
- tape
- a pourable material such as popcorn
- *Final Assessment Master 36*, Measure, Measure, Measure

Timing

45 min

Overall Goals and Key Concepts

- learning the basics of *The Geometer's Sketchpad*®

Materials

- *Assessment Master 32*, A3.6A Make a Seasonal Picture Using *The Geometer's Sketchpad*®
- *The Geometer's Sketchpad*® software
- data projector hooked up to computer

Timing

75–150 min

3.5G Surface Area and Volume of a Cylinder

Student Resource pp. 163–164

Teaching Suggestions

Provide each group with sheets of paper (about 8″ by 14″) and tape. Have the students complete this activity in pairs or groups. The tubes can be filled to further demonstrate that their volumes are different when rolled in different directions. You could demonstrate this for the whole class. Popcorn works well for this demonstration. Students could hypothesize what dimensions would produce the maximum volume for a given surface area.

Final Assessment

Distribute *Final Assessment Master 36*, Measure, Measure, Measure, and have the students complete it. Collect and mark it for summative assessment.

3.6 Relations in Euclidean Geometry

If the number of computers is limited, Section 3.6 can be combined with several other topics in this student resource. The students can alternate during the class. Suggestions include: Activities 2.1–2.3 Algebra, Activities 3.1–3.5 Measurement.

3.6A Introduction to *The Geometer's Sketchpad*®

Student Resource pp. 165–169

Teaching Suggestions

It is useful to check features such as choosing **Preferences** from the **Display** menu on a regular basis for labelling and precision of numbers. As well, daily recaps of significant features and techniques are helpful.

Encourage the students to work in pairs, alternating at the keyboard to investigate the introductory features of this software. Each subtopic requires consolidation of ideas and practice before moving on. Using the data projector to show the students what their screens should look like as you proceed step by step is invaluable. Invite student tutors (if available) or other teachers to join you on the first day. They can be extremely helpful, as there will be many questions. Some students will require additional time.

Demonstrate and have the students try the following, making these notes in their workbook.

> To Clear the Screen:
> a) **Edit, Select All, Delete**
> b) **Control-Z** repeatedly
> c) Select the items with the **Selection Tool** and **Delete**

> To select several objects at once, hold down the **SHIFT** key while selecting objects.

To draw horizontal and vertical segments (lines), hold down the **SHIFT** key while constructing the segment (line).

It is necessary to **Construct Polygon Interior** before **Measuring** the area and perimeter. As they learn each new idea, encourage the students to make notes and diagrams on the pages for use next time. Allowing the students to use their notes throughout the section and on assessment may be enough incentive to write. There are ample opportunities to play throughout this section, as each student becomes familiar with the features of the program. Animation on student resource page 169 can be optional, although many students will enjoy using this feature and will make great use of it in later sections.

Assessment
Distribute *Assessment Master 32*, A3.6A Make a Seasonal Picture Using *The Geometer's Sketchpad®*, and have the students complete it. Collect and mark it for formative assessment.

Specific Expectations
MG3.01, MG3.04, MG3.05

Overall Goals and Key Concepts
- use *The Geometer's Sketchpad®* to show a Euclidean proof of ASTT
- extend this idea to the sum of interior angles of other polygons

Materials
- *Assessment Master 33*, A3.6A Make a Seasonal Picture Using *The Geometer's Sketchpad®*
- *The Geometer's Sketchpad®* software

Timing
75 min

Related Resources
MATHPOWER™ 9, Ontario Edition, Blackline Masters Master 10.1 (Select)

3.6B The Sum of the Angles of a Polygon

Student Resource pp. 170–171

Teaching Suggestions
Have the students work through Part 1. Some of them will require considerable help to remember how to find the menus etc. Some students will animate the diagram. Students continue with Part 2, drawing a quadrilateral and measuring the sum of the interior angles.

Many of the activities that follow can be animated to demonstrate multiple solutions with a common result.

Common Errors
Some students will complete the activity and still not be able to describe what the activity "taught" them. For this reason, class demonstrations using a data projector or equivalent, with a verbal and written review of the idea, will solidify concepts for individuals and for the class as a whole.

Specific Expectations
MG3.01, MG3.04,
MG3.05, AG1.03, RE1.04,
RE1.05, AG2.01, AG2.02,
AG2.03, AG2.04, AG3.01,
AG3.02, AG3.04, AG3.05,
NA3.03

Overall Goals and Key Concepts
- find the sum of the interior angles of any polygon, and connect this new concept with the fundamental expectations of Units 1 and 2

Timing
75 min

Related Resources
MATHPOWER™ 9, Ontario Edition, Blackline Masters
Master 10.1 (Select)

3.6C The Sum of the Interior Angles of a Polygon: Activity

Student Resource pp. 172–175

Teaching Suggestions

Students will need to understand diagonals of polygons to complete this activity. It is not necessary to use *The Geometer's Sketchpad®;* the conclusions will be based on Activity 3.6B (ASTT). Ask the students to complete a chart (gather data) as they go, and, then, draw the graph (scatter plot and line of best fit), develop an equation, and make conclusions. (This again reviews the skills learned in Units 1 and 2, such as $y = mx + b$ and solutions of linear equations).

This activity could be used as an assessment, since it does an excellent job of consolidating many expectations from the course into one rich problem.

Common Errors
- Ensure that the students have labelled their axes correctly, i.e., number of sides vs. sum of the angles
- Emphasize in question 5, on student resource page 175, that the students use the equation that was developed.

Specific Expectations
MG3.01, MG3.04, MG3.05

Overall Goals and Key Concepts
- demonstrate the Exterior Angles of a Triangle theorem and the sum of exterior angles of polygons

Materials
- *The Geometer's Sketchpad®* software

Timing
75 min

Related Resources
MATHPOWER™ 9, Ontario Edition, Blackline Masters
Master 10.1 (Select)

3.6D Exterior Angles of a Polygon

Student Resource pp. 176–178

Teaching Suggestions

Students will work at varied paces through the constructions and proofs. Summarize the results of the sum of exterior angles of any polygon. Additional practice may be necessary.

Common Errors

Circulate and talk to the students about their conclusions.

Specific Expectations
MG3.01, MG3.04, MG3.05

Overall Goals and Key
Concepts
• use *The Geometer's
Sketchpad*® to "prove"
CA, SA, ASTT, and OAT

Materials
• *Assessment Master 33*,
Angle Relations:
Supplementary Angles
• *The Geometer's
Sketchpad*® software

Timing
45 min

Related Resources
MATHPOWER™ 9,
*Ontario Edition,
Blackline Masters*
Master 10.1 (Select)

3.6E Using Dynamic Geometry to "Prove" Geometric Theorems: Angles

Student Resource pp. 179–180

Teaching Suggestions
Again, timing will vary from student to student. Students may want to refer to Activity 3.6B, ASTT, to model their solutions and conclusions. One page of practice using these theorems is provided on student resource page 180, but supplementary exercises will be necessary to practise the recognition and applications of the Euclidean properties developed.

Assessment
Distribute *Assessment Master 33*, A3.6E Angle Relations: Supplementary Angles, and have the students complete it. Collect and mark it for formative assessment.

Specific Expectations
MG3.01

Overall Goals and Key
Concepts
• use *The Geometer's
Sketchpad*® to do
"proofs" of parallelism
theorems (TPT F, Z, C)

Materials
• *Assessment Master 34*,
A3.6F Angle Relations
• *The Geometer's
Sketchpad*® software

Timing
45 min

Related Resources
MATHPOWER™ 9,
*Ontario Edition,
Blackline Masters*
Master 10.2 (Select)

3.6F Using Dynamic Geometry to "Prove" Geometric Theorems: Parallel Lines

Student Resource pp. 181–182

Teaching Suggestions
Define the term **transversal** before beginning the activity.

By measuring the angles formed by parallel lines and the transversal, the students should see patterns for equal and supplementary angles. One page of practice using these theorems is provided on student resource page 182, but supplementary exercises will be necessary to practise the recognition and the applications of the Euclidean properties developed.

Common Errors
Students may need review in the construction of parallel lines from Activity 3.6A.

Assessment
Distribute *Assessment Master 34*, A3.6F Angle Relations, and have the students complete it. Collect and mark it for formative assessment.

Specific Expectations
MG3.01, MG3.03,
MG3.04, MG3.05

**Overall Goals and Key
Concepts**
- review the properties of
  the interior and exterior
  angles of quadrilaterals
- discover the properties of
  the diagonals of rectangles
  and squares

Materials
- *Assessment Master 35,
  A3.6G* Prove a Theorem
- *The Geometer's
  Sketchpad®* software

Timing
45+ min

3.6G Using Dynamic Geometry to Look at Quadrilaterals

Student Resource pp. 183–184

Teaching Suggestions

Only the topic of the properties of the diagonals of a rectangle is new here, the others being review. The review provides "comfortable" practice with *The Geometer's Sketchpad®* plus reinforcement of the properties.

The construction of a rectangle can be achieved using perpendicular and parallel lines, hiding the lines, and connecting the vertices with segments. The formal construction of squares is challenging for many students. It is quite effective "adjusting" a rectangle to make all sides equal. In either case, extra time will be required to ensure that the students do, in fact, have rectangles and squares to analyse. The latest version of *The Geometer's Sketchpad®* has scripts which produce rectangles and squares directly on the screen.

Common Errors

Circulate to be sure students have formed the correct shapes and conclusions.

Assessment

Distribute *Assessment Master 35, A3.6G* Prove a Theorem, and have the students complete it. Collect and mark it for formative assessment. The students may use their books/notes to complete this.

Specific Expectations
MG3.02, MG3.04, MG3.05

**Overall Goals and Key
Concepts**
- draw a perpendicular
  bisector
- learn the circle centres

Materials
- *Assessment Master 36,
  A3.6G* Prove a Theorem
- *The Geometer's
  Sketchpad®* software
- data projector

Timing
75 min

3.6H Circumcentre of a Triangle

3.6I Triangle Centres and Their Properties

Student Resource pp. 185–188

Teaching Suggestions

Formal construction of the circumcentre of a triangle is provided. The other centres follow similar guidelines. The incircle is constructed by using the circle tool. A formal construction of the incircle can be done at your discretion. Students will need help with these constructions. Again, it would be prudent to review the construction of perpendicular lines from Activity 3.6A.

The construction from Activity 3.6I could be done as a class using the data projector. The more technologically aware students may help their peers. It may be of interest to note the appearance of the Euler line segment using the three centres: **centroid**, **circumcentre**, and **orthocentre**. All three will always lie on a straight line in a fixed ratio (1:2). More practice is necessary.

As before, dragging (animating) diagrams will demonstrate the consistency of the constructions and properties.

Common Errors

Review conclusions about circle centres as a class. Some student confuse the different circle centres.

Specific Expectations

NA3.04, NA4.01, NA4.02, NA4.03, AG1.03

Overall Goals and Key Concepts

- use *The Geometer's Sketchpad®* to review and consolidate other aspects of the course, such as pi, the Pythagorean theorem, and equations of lines

Materials

- *The Geometer's Sketchpad®* software

Timing

150 min

Materials

- *The Geometer's Sketchpad®* software
- *Assessment Master 37,* Sketchpad Assessment

Timing

75 min

Section 3.7 Relations and *The Geometer's Sketchpad®*

3.7A Pi Demonstration (Again)

3.7B The Pythagorean Theorem Using *The Geometer's Sketchpad®*

3.7C Equations of Lines and *The Geometer's Sketchpad®*

3.7D Family of Lines: Activity

Student Resource pp. 189–192

Teaching Suggestions

Do not do these activities for a whole period. These activities are better done in combination with other end-of-year activities such as EQAO, review of the year's work, review of Unit 3, or Final Assessment. Having computers in the classroom gives the students an opportunity to move from their desks to a computer to do one of the four activities on each of four days as well as doing some of the tasks mentioned above.

Each task presents a second view of a previously studied concept with the use of dynamic geometry, *The Geometer's Sketchpad®*. Activity 3.7A revisits the relationship of circumference and diameter of Activity 3.3A; Activity 3.7B revisits the concepts of the Pythagorean theorem in Activity 3.4; and Activities 3.7C and 3.7D revisit the properties of $y = mx + b$ and families of lines.

In Activity 3.7A, to construct a line through two points, it is necessary to select the **Line Tool** on the vertical tool bar. These activities can be extended to meet the needs of any and all students.

A3 Sketchpad Assessment

Teaching Suggestions

Distribute *Assessment Master 37,* Sketchpad Assessment, and have the students complete it. Collect and mark it for summative assessment. Allow the students to use their books and notes for this assessment.

At the teacher check points, the teacher will correct any errors (or assist the students in correcting them) and mark accordingly. In this way, the students can proceed with the correct screen.

A3.1E Area and Perimeter

Part A
Directions: State three careers that would require you to find the perimeter or area of something. Explain how or why you would need to find these (area or perimeter). Be specific.

1.

2.

3.

Part B
Andrea and Jon are making repairs to the outside of their home. For each item being fixed, circle whether they need to find the area or the perimeter, in order to purchase the necessary supplies for that job.

paint the deck	area	perimeter
install aluminum siding on the garden shed	area	perimeter
replace the trim on the exterior windows	area	perimeter
fence the dog pen	area	perimeter
replace the railing on the deck	area	perimeter
add topsoil in the garden	area	perimeter

Part C

Directions: Give a full solution for each question. Include formulas and units as needed.

1. Find the area of each shape.

    a)

    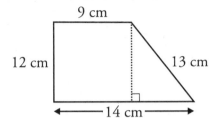

    b)

    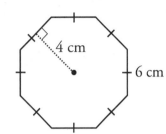

2. Find the perimeter of each shape.

    a)

    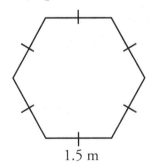

    b)

    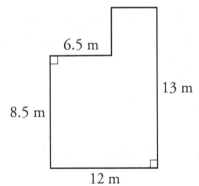

3. The following yard needs sod.
   a) Find the area of the yard.

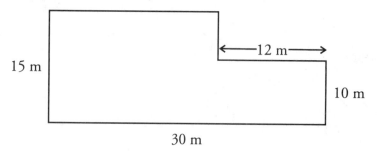

   b) Find the cost to sod the yard if sod costs $2.59/m² plus 15% tax.

4. The sides of a square pool area are 14 m long. The pool is to be enclosed by a fence with a gate, 1.2 m wide.
   a) Draw and label a diagram and find the amount of fencing needed.

   b) Find the cost of the fence if fencing costs $14.29/m plus 15% taxes.

   c) This fencing is on sale for 35% off. How much will you save on this project if you buy the fencing on sale?

5. Draw and label the dimensions of a shape that has the given characteristics. (You may use the graph paper if you wish. Be sure to label the question and the dimensions clearly.)

a) a square whose perimeter is 32 cm

b) a rectangle (not a square), whose area is 32 m^2

c) a rectangle whose perimeter is 35 m and whose width is 7.5 m

d) a triangle whose area is 40 cm^2 (Label the base and the height.)

A3.3B Circles

$C = \pi d \quad A = \pi r^2$

1. Find the circumference of the given circle.

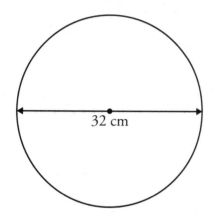

32 cm

2. Find the area of this circle.

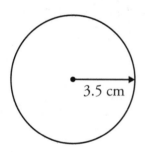

3.5 cm

3. What do you know about this number?

$$\pi_\pi \; \pi_\pi \; \pi_\pi \; \pi_\pi \; \pi_\pi \; \pi_\pi$$

4. This large, fancy window was designed for the front of the town hall, but cost is an issue.

   a) The window needs oak moulding (trim) around the edge. Moulding costs $12.50/m. What would be the cost of the moulding, excluding taxes?

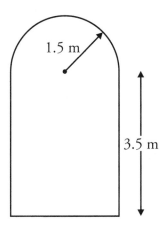

   b) The glass for the window costs $13.75/m². How much would the glass cost for the window, excluding taxes?

   c) What is the total cost of the glass and moulding for this window if you include PST and GST of 15%?

A3.3C Area and Perimeter

1. Determine the area of the shaded region. Show all your work.

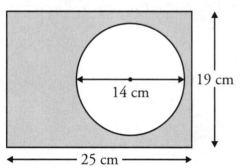

2. The window shown needs wood trim around the outside edge.
   a) Determine the amount needed.

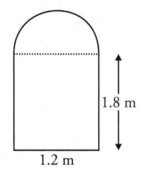

   b) Trim comes in lengths of 0.8 m and costs $2.50 for each length.
      How much would the trim cost, excluding taxes?

A3.4B Pythagorean Theorem

1. Determine the length of the missing side in the triangle below.

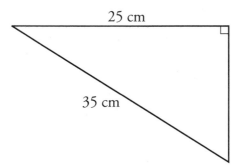

25 cm

35 cm

2. A windowsill is 3.5 m above the ground. If the bottom of a ladder is 1.7 m from the base of the wall and the top of the ladder is leaning against the windowsill, how long is the ladder? Include a diagram.

A3.5B Paint the Walls

1. The model represents a room in a house.
   You are going to paint all four walls and
   the ceiling.
   a) Draw and label the **net** of the room.

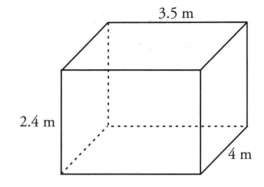

b) Calculate the surface area of the walls to be painted.

c) A can of paint will cover 30 m². If a can of paint costs $28.50,
determine the total cost, including taxes, to paint the room.

A3.5E Surface Area and Volume

1. This is a model of Marina's tent.
   a) Find the volume of the tent.

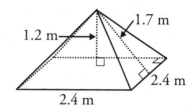

   b) Marina and her two friends want to camp out in the tent. Each person requires 0.75 m³ of air space. Does the volume of the tent provide this?

2. How much canvas, including the floor, is used to make this tent? (*Hint:* Draw and label the net.)

A3.6A Make a Seasonal Picture Using
The Geometer's Sketchpad®

Use *The Geometer's Sketchpad*® to create a picture.
Your picture must be seasonal in nature.

It must include each of the items listed below and will be marked as indicated.
If you receive help from your teacher, a mark will be deducted.

You may use your notes or book.

If there is a blank beside an item below, write in the blank where this item can be found on your picture.

- circle (1)   coloured (1)

- parallel lines (2)   _____   with hidden extensions (2)

- perpendicular lines (2)   _____   with hidden extensions (2)

- a labelled line segment with its length shown (2)

- a labelled angle with the size of the angle shown (2)

- a labelled polygon with the area of the polygon shown (2)

- animation (2 bonus)

- interest, creativity, special effects (2)

Name _____   Date _____

A3.6E Angle Relations: Supplementary Angles

Go to a computer and open up *The Geometer's Sketchpad*® software.
Use the computer to demonstrate the property of

Supplementary Angles.

You have 10 minutes to do this. For bonus marks, you can animate your result.

If you have any difficulties, you can ask for help, but marks will be deducted.

When you have finished, ask your teacher to evaluate your computer work.

Marking (Each is out of 2 marks.)

- Knows the theorem.

- Knows how to use *The Geometer's Sketchpad*® to draw the diagram.

- Can find the angles.

- Can find the sum of the angles.

- Knows how to use *The Geometer's Sketchpad*® to "prove" the theorem is always true.

- Bonus mark for animation

Additional Comments:

Total:

Name _____   Date _____

A3.6F Angle Relations

1. Find the value of each variable. Find the angles indicated. Show your work.

a)

$x =$ _____

$y =$ _____

b)

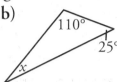

$x =$ _____

c)

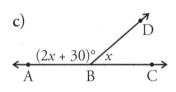

$x =$ _____

$\angle ABD =$ _____

d)

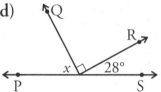

$x =$ _____

e)

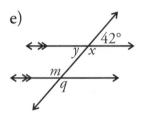

$x =$ _____

$y =$ _____

$m =$ _____

$q =$ _____

f)

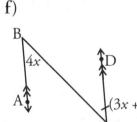

$x =$ _____

$\angle ABC =$ _____

$\angle BCD =$ _____

2. Go to a computer and open up *The Geometer's Sketchpad*® software. Use the computer to "prove" the Angle Sum Triangle Theorem. You have 10 minutes to do this. For bonus marks, you can animate your result. If you have any difficulties, you can ask for help, but marks will be deducted. When you have finished, ask your teacher to evaluate your computer work.

Marking (Each is out of 2 marks.)

• Knows the theorem.

• Knows how to use *The Geometer's Sketchpad*® to draw the diagram.

• Can find the angles.

• Can find the sum of the angles.

• Knows how to use *The Geometer's Sketchpad*® to "prove" the theorem is always true.

• Bonus mark for animation.

A3.6G Prove a Theorem

1. Using *The Geometer's Sketchpad*®, construct quadrilateral ABCD.
   Find the midpoint of each side and label as shown in the diagram below.
   Join the midpoints of the sides in order to form quadrilateral EFGH.

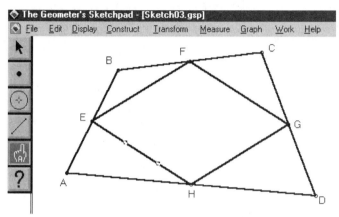

2. Measure the slope and the length of each of EF, FG, GH, and HE.
   Complete the chart below for 3 different quadrilaterals by dragging a vertex.

Quadrilateral	Segment	Slope	Length
1	EF		
	GH		
	FG		
	HE		
2	EF		
	GH		
	FG		
	HE		
3	EF		
	GH		
	FG		
	HE		

3. Describe what happens to the measurements as the quadrilateral changes.

4. Conclusions and Observations: Fill in the blanks.
The lines joining the midpoints of the sides of a quadrilateral form a

quadrilateral whose opposite sides are _____ and _____.
The quadrilateral formed is a parallelogram.

Use your theorem to fill in the blanks below.

5. Given quadrilateral ABCD shown with midpoints Q, R, S, and T.
   a) Name any parallel line segments.

   _____ is parallel to _____

   b) Name any equal line segments
   (not already indicated).

   _____ = _____

   _____ = _____

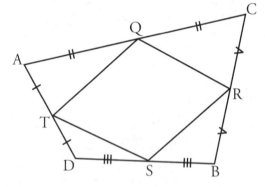

6. Given quadrilateral PQRS shown with midpoints K, L, M, and N,
   ∠LKM = 30°, and ∠KLM = 130°.
   a) Write the measure of ∠KMN.

   _____

   Give your reason.

   b) Write the measure of ∠LMK.

   _____

   Give your reason.

   c) Write the measure of ∠MKN.

   _____

   Give your reason.

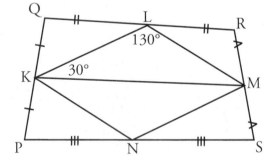

Unit 3 Final Assessment:
Measure, Measure, Measure

Complete solutions, including written statements, are required for full marks.

1. Determine the area of the shaded region.

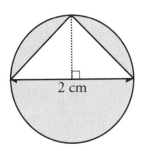

2. Draw a circle around the solids that are prisms.

3. a) What is the relationship between the volume of a prism and the volume of a pyramid?

b) Explain how you determined this relationship in class.

4. a) Determine the volume of a classroom that measures 10 m × 7 m × 3 m.

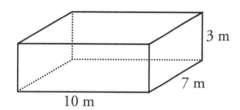

b) Air quality control requires that, for comfort, each student must have 5.4 m³ of air space. How many students can the classroom in part a) hold comfortably?

5. Each time a dump truck filled with sand unloads, it makes
   a pile in the shape of a cone (a circle-based pyramid).
   Each pile has a diameter of 4.5 m and a height of 2 m.
   a) Draw and label a sketch of the pile of sand.

   b) Determine the volume of sand in the pile.

   c) If the area of the base of the box of the truck is 14 m², what is the height
      of the box?

6. When Paul walks to school, he sometimes takes
   a shortcut at one of the corners. He can either
   walk on the sidewalk, as shown, OR cut
   diagonally across the corner, as in the diagram.
   a) How long is the shortcut that Paul
      sometimes takes?
      (The shortcut is shown by the broken line.)

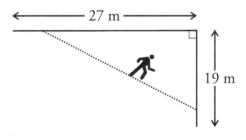

   b) How much distance does Paul save by "cutting the corner"?

7. The diagram at the right is of the Great Pyramid of
   Khufu. It has a square base. An archaeologist wishes to
   seal the stone surface to protect it from eroding.
   a) Draw a net of the pyramid, including the base.

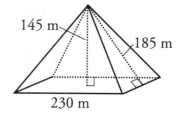

145 m

185 m

230 m

b) Determine the visible surface area of the pyramid.
   (Do not include base.)

c) The cost of sealing the stone is $5.00/m².
   Find the cost of sealing the visible surface area of this pyramid.

d) Do you think that the Great Pyramids of Egypt should be preserved with a
   chemical sealant? Explain.

8. You want to plant a garden at a back corner of the yard. There is already a fence that can border two of the four sides of your garden. You have 12 m of fencing for the other two sides. Determine the dimensions of the garden with the largest possible area.

a) Make a table of the possible dimensions and the area.

Length	Width	Area

You may use a graphing calculator, or the grid given below to complete parts b) and c) below.

b) Draw a graph showing the length and the area of the garden.

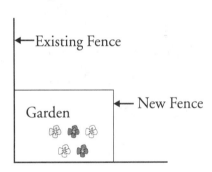

c) Using your graph, and your data, state the dimensions that would give the maximum possible area of the garden. Justify your answer.

Unit 3 Final Assessment: Sketchpad Assessment

From the **Display** menu select **Preferences**.
For the **Distance** units select **cm**.
For every **Precision** select **units**.
Press **More . . . .** For the **Screen Resolution** select **38 dots/cm**.
Press **Continue** and then press ✔**OK**
From the **Graph** menu select **Show Grid**.

Instructions and Checklist
Be sure to have your teacher check each section where shown

Construction	Marks	Observations, Measurements, Comments
1. Draw a line with a slope of 2, through point C(1, –3).	2	
2. Construct a line from E(0, 4), perpendicular to the line in step 1 above.	2	
Construct the point at the intersection of this line and the line in step 1 above. Label it F.	1	
3. Construct segment C(1, –3) and E(0, 4) to form ΔCEF. Colour the interior of ΔCEF blue, and find its area.	2	Area$_{\Delta CEF}$ = _____
Teacher Check Number 1	/7	
4. Construct the midpoint of the hypotenuse of ΔCEF. Label it O.	1	
5. Construct a circle with centre O and radius OC.	1	
What other points on your diagram lie on the circumference of your circle?	1	Points _____
Circle one of the following. The circle with centre O is called		
• the centroid		
• the orthocentre		
• the circumcentre	1	
Teacher Check Number 2	/4	

6. Colour the circle yellow and find its area.	1	
Place on the circumference of the circle a point in the third or fourth quadrant. Label it H.	1	Area$_{circle}$ = _____
7. Construct △CEH. Colour it red. Measure ∠CHE.	2	∠CHE = _____
8. Drag H along the circumference of the circle.	2	Observation:
Bonus: Animate point H to move around the circumference. Be sure you have unselected all points. What happens to ∠CHE?	(1) Bonus	
Final Teacher Check	/6	

Conclusion:

A triangle inscribed in a semicircle is a _____ triangle.

Use what you learned in step 8 above to answer the following:

a) ∠ABC = _____°   **b)** ∠CAB = 48°

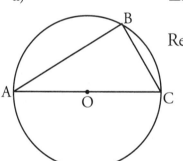

Reason:

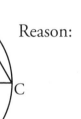

∠BCA = _____°

Reason:

c) ∠BAD + ∠BCD = _____°

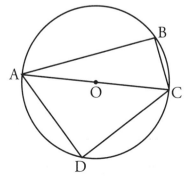

Reason:

Student Resource Answers

Unit 3 Relationships in Geometry

3.1 Area and Perimeter

3.1A Rectangles
p. 130

A = length × width
$P = 2 \times$ length $+ 2 \times$ width
$\quad = 2$ (length + width)

1. a) $A = 216$ cm^2; $P = 60$ cm
   b) $A = 225$ m^2; $P = 60$ m
   c) $A = 74$ cm^2; $P = 42$ cm
2. Answers will vary

3.1B Area and Perimeter: Class Activity p. 131

1., 2., 3. Answers will vary.
4. Area
5. Perimeter
6. Answers will vary. For example, carpenter and interior designer.

3.1C Area and Perimeter: Combined Shapes
p. 132

half; half

$A_{\text{triangle}} = \dfrac{1}{2}lw$

Practice

1. a) 40 cm^2 b) 38.5 cm^2
2. a) 101.92 cm$^2 + 58.80$ cm$^2 = 160.72$ cm^2
   b) 0.75 m$^2 + 2.25$ m$^2 = 3.00$ m^2
   c) 6 cm$^2 + 24$ cm$^2 + 9$ cm$^2 = 39$ cm^2

3.1D Area and Perimeter: Applications p. 133

You need to know the dimensions of the room in order to calculate the areas of walls and floor in order to buy the correct amount of paint, etc.

1. a)

   2.7 m [ ] 2.7 m [ ] 2.7 m [ ] 2.7 m [ ]
   3.5 m   3.5 m   4.0 m   4.0 m

   $A_{\text{total}} = 40.5$ m^2
   b) 3   c) $113.68
   d) Answers may vary. For example, because he will not paint the doors and windows, he may use less paint than he expected, or he may need to apply two coats of paint and use more paint than expected.
2. a) 22.95 m$^2 + 11.47$ m$^2 = 34.42$ m^2
   b) 18   c) $1033.97
   d) 26.6 m   e) 9

f) Answers may vary. For example, she may not put moulding on all edges of the floor if there are things that are situated there. She will not put moulding across doorways.
3. a) 11   b) $252.37
   c) Answers may vary. For example, she may want to match the patterns and therefore there will be waste. She will not require wallpaper for windows and doors.
4. 18.93 m^2

3.1E Area Assignment: Redecorate a Room
p. 136

All answers will vary.

3.2 Maximum Areas

3.2A A Swimmingly Great Problem p. 137

Problem

Step 1
Answers will vary, for example, a square pool with dimensions 15 m × 15 m.
Step 2
1. a) i) 60 m   ii) 29 m^2
   b) i) 60 m   ii) 200 m^2
Step 3
1. Answers may vary. For example,

Perimeter (m)	Length (m)	Width (m)	Area (m^2)
60	30	0	0
60	29	1	29
60	28	2	56
60	25	5	125
60	22	8	176
60	19	11	209
60	17	13	221
60	16	14	224
60	15	15	225
60	14	16	224
60	13	17	221
60	10	20	200
60	8	22	176
60	7	23	161
60	6	24	144
60	5	25	125
60	4	26	104
60	3	27	81
60	2	28	56
60	1	29	29
60	0	30	0

No, once you get to 15 m × 15 m, the chart repeats itself.

3., 4.

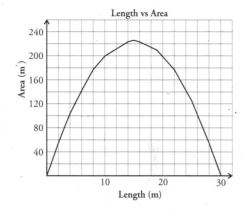

Length vs Area

5. a) 15 m × 15 m

b)

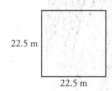

15 m

15 m

c) A pool that has a perimeter of 60 m yields the greatest area with dimensions 15m × 15m. This is the highest point on the graph. Thus, it is the maximum area.

6. Answers will vary.

7. 22.5 m × 22.5 m

22.5 m

22.5 m

8. Answers may vary. For example, length to be long for racing, keeping people away from weeds, and keeping people in a shallow area.

3.2B Down the Garden Path: Maximum Area
p. 141

1. 160 cm × 160 cm

2., 3.

Perimeter (m)	Length (m)	Width (m)	Area (m²)
640	0	320	0
640	20	300	6 000
640	40	280	11 200
640	60	260	15 600
640	80	240	19 200
640	100	220	22 000
640	120	200	24 000
640	140	180	25 200
640	160	160	25 600
640	180	140	25 200
640	200	120	24 000
640	220	100	22 000
640	240	80	19 200
640	260	60	15 600
640	280	40	11 200
640	300	20	6 000
640	320	0	0

4. a), b)

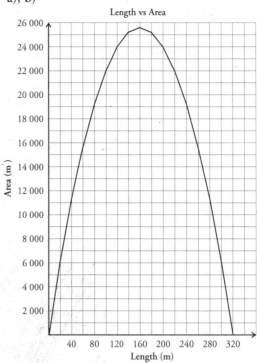

Length vs Area

5. The best dimensions for this garden is 160 m by 160 m. Explanations may vary but should include references to the graph.

7. Answers may vary.

3.3 Circles

3.3A Pi Development
p. 143

Hypothesis
- linear
- positive
- as the diameter increases the circumference increases
- (0, 0) is in the set of data
- continuous

1. a), b), c), d) Answers will vary.
   e) They are all close to 3.14.

2. a), b) Answers may vary slightly.

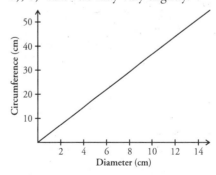

3. $m = 3.14$; $b = 0$

4. $y = 3.14x$; $c = 3.14d$

5. a) pi
   b) circle
   c) area: $A = \pi r^2$;
   circumference: $c = \pi d$ or $c = 2\pi r$

3.3B Circle: Area and Circumference · p. 145

$A = \pi r^2$; $C = \pi d$ or $2\pi r$

1. $A = 7850$ cm^2; $C = 314$ cm
2. a) $A = 803.84$ cm^2; $C = 100.48$ cm
   b) 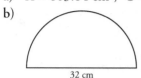 $A = 401.92$ cm^2; $C = 82.24$ cm

   32 cm

3. a) Answers may vary; for example, the area of the sign is needed to determine the amount of paint required.
   b) 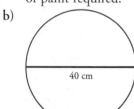 $A = 1256$ cm^2

   40 cm

   c) 126 cans

4. a) 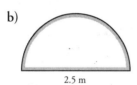   b)

   2.5 m   2.5 m

   c) 7.85 m

5. a) 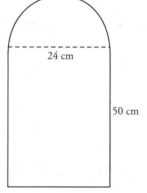   b) 1652.16 cm
                              c) 161.68 cm

   24 cm

   50 cm

6. 30 000 cm^2 – 1413 cm^2 = 28 587 cm^2

3.3C Areas of Combined Shapes · p. 148

1. 32.13 cm^2 2. 43.13 cm^2

3.3D Round and Round and Round... · p. 149

Problem
The answer is c). A human could wriggle under the string. (The difference in the radius is 31.8 cm.)

3.4 Pythagorean Theorem

3.4A Pythagorean Theorem Puzzle · p. 150

Conclusion
squares, equal, square, hypotenuse

3.4B Using the Pythagorean Theorem · p. 151

Example 1
$a = 8$; $b = 15$; $h^2 = 289$; $h = 17$ cm
A square root symbol means that only the positive square root value is considered.

Example 2
$a = 2.5$; $h = 7$; $b = 6.54$ m

Example 3
$a^2 + b^2 = h^2$; $0.5^2 + 4^2 = l^2$; $l = 4.03$ m

Example 4
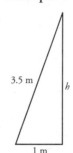
$a^2 + b^2 = h^2$;
$1^2 + h^2 = 3.5^2$;
$h = 3.35$ m

3.5 m h

1 m

3.4C More Pythagoras · p. 153

1. a) 32.45 cm   b) 243 cm^2
2. Answers may vary. The answers should show the squares on the sides and the hypotenuse, and a written explanation.

3.5 Three-Dimensional Geometry

3.5A Nets and Solids · p. 154

a) a) <—> a); b) <—> f); c) <—> h);
   d) <—> c); e) <—> d) and j); f) <—> b)

b) a) <—> e); b) <—> b); c) <—> g);
   d) <—> i); e) <—> a); f) <—> j)

3.5B Surface Area of Prisms · p. 155

1. a) triangular prism
   b) 15 cm
   c)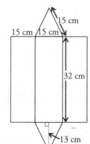

   15 cm
   15 cm 15 cm
   32 cm
   13 cm

   d) 1635 cm^2
   e) $408.75

2. a)

   9.42 m
   22.5 m
   3 m

   b) 226.08 m^2
   c) 6
   d) $241.50

3.5C Three-Dimensional Geometry: Surface Area
p. 157

Name of Solid	Net of Solid Made Up of ___ ◻ s + ___ ◯ s + ___ △ s	Surface Area of Solid
rectangular prism	6; 0; 0	222 cm²
triangular prism	3; 0; 2	498 cm²
cylinder	1; 2; 0	579.33 cm²
pyramid	1; 0; 4	33 cm²

3.5D Volume of a Prism
p. 158

Example 1

$V = (5 \times 3)(12)$
$= 180$
Volume is 180 cm³.

Example 2

$V = (\pi r^2)(h)$
$= (3.14 \times 2.5^2)(3.5)$
$= 68.69$
Volume is 68.69 m³.

3.5E Volume of a Pyramid
p. 159

Process All answers will vary.

Conclusion

They should be in sentence form such as: The volume of a pyramid is $\frac{1}{3}$ the volume of a prism with the same height and a congruent base.

1. The volume of the pyramid is one third of the volume of the prism with a congruent base and the same height.

2. $V = \dfrac{Bh}{3}$

   Answers may vary. For example: The volume of a pyramid is the area of the base times the height divided by 3.

3.5F Minimum Surface Area: Rectangular Prism
p. 160

1. Answers may vary slightly. The following table contains all the whole number values possible.

Area of Base	Height	Surface Area	Volume
1	64	258	64
2	32	196	64
4	16	168	64
4	16	136	64
8	8	160	64
8	8	112	64
16	4	168	64
16	4	112	64
16	4	96	64
32	2	196	64
32	2	136	64
32	2	112	64
64	1	258	64
64	1	196	64
64	1	168	64
64	1	160	64

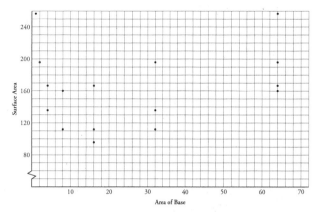

Conclusions

3. 4 cm × 4 cm × 4 cm: The point (16, 96) is the lowest point on the graph and thus represents the least surface area.

4. 1 cm × 1 cm × 64 cm: The point (1, 258) is the highest point on the graph and represents the greatest surface area.

5. Answers will vary. For example, packing items in boxes and storing boxes

6. cube shape, or as close to a cube as is possible

7. a) 2 × 2 × 2; cube of volume 8
   b) 3 × 3 × 3; cube of volume 27
   c) 4 × 4 × 4; cube of volume 64
   d) 5 × 5 × 5; cube of volume 125
   e) 3 × 4 × 5: This is the closest to a cube with volume of 60 cubic units.

8. a) No; usually, these containers are not in the shape of a cube. They are usually more rectangular.
   b) Answers will vary. For example, the stores couldn't stack as many on the shelves, unless they stacked the boxes upwards. Also, the boxes are built to accommodate the shape of the containers inside them. Some boxes are built to give room to write on the outside.

3.5G Surface Area and Volume of a Cylinder
p. 163

1. through 7. Answers may vary. Assume standard $8\frac{1}{2}'' \times 11''$ sheet of paper used.

8. a) Surface area: The size of the paper did not change.
   b) Volume: The area of the base and the height change when the sheet of paper is rolled in different directions.

9. When the height is equal to the diameter: This result is similar to the result in Activity 3.5F (cube).

3.6 Relations in Euclidean Geometry

3.6A Introduction to *The Geometer's Sketchpad®*
p. 165

All answers will vary.
I The Toolbox
Practice
1. a)

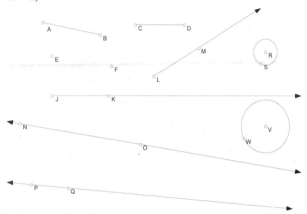

3.6B The Sum of the Angles of a Polygon
p. 170

Most answers will vary.
Part 1
3. 180°
4. 180°
Observations
The measurements of the angles change; the sum of the angles does not change.
Conclusion
The sum of the angles in a triangle is 180°.
Part 2
3. 360°

m∠LSK = 73.0°
m∠SKI = 107.0°
m∠KIL = 104.3°
m∠ILS = 75.7°
m∠LSK + m∠SKI + m∠KIL + m∠ILS = 360.0°

4. 360°
Observations
The measurements of the angles change; the sum of the angles does not change.
Conclusion
The sum of the angles in a quadrilateral is 360°.

3.6C The Sum of the Interior Angles of a Polygon: Activity
p. 172

Part 1
1. a), b)

b) 2
c) 360°; ASTT = 180°. The number of triangles formed multiplied by the sum of the angles in a triangle equals the sum of the angles in a quadrilateral.
d) The number of triangles formed is two fewer than the number of sides of the quadrilateral.
2. a), b)

b) 3   c) 540°
d) The number of triangles formed is two fewer than the number of sides of the pentagon.
Part 2
Hypothesis
• linear
• positive
• As the number of sides increases, the sum of the angles increases.

Polygon and Number of Sides	Number of Triangles Formed by Diagonals	Sum of Interior Angles	First Differences
Triangle 3	1	180	
			180
Quadrilateral 4	2	360	
			180
Pentagon 5	3	540	
			180
Hexagon 6	4	720	
			180
Heptagon 7	5	900	
			180
Octagon 8	6	1080	

The first differences are equal and positive.
The relationship is linear and the correlation is positive.

Scatter Plot and Line of Best Fit

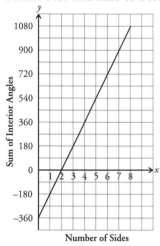

1. a) $m = 180$; $b = -360$, or Sum = $180(n) - 360$, where n is the number of sides.
   b) $y = 180x - 360$
2. a) $1260°$ b) $1620°$
3. 10
4. The number of sides would not be a whole number; this is impossible.
5.

The sum of the interior angles of a polygon with 9 sides	$n = 9$ $S = 180n - 360$ $\ = 180(9) - 360$ $\ = 1620 - 360$ $\ = 1260$
The sum of the interior angles of a polygon with 11 sides	1620
The number of sides in a polygon with an interior angle sum of 1440	10

6. To find the sum of the interior angles of a polygon, multiply the number of sides of the polygon by 180° and subtract 360°, or multiply 180 by 2 less than the number of sides.

3.6D Exterior Angles of a Polygon   p. 176

Most answers will vary.
Part 1
2. b) $360°$
3. $360°$
Observations
The measurement of the exterior angles changes; the sum of the exterior angles does not change.
Conclusions
The sum of the exterior angles of a triangle is 360°.
Part 2
2. b) $360°$
3. $360°$

Observations
The measurement of the exterior angles changes; the sum of the exterior angles does not change.
Conclusions
The sum of the exterior angles of a quadrilateral is 360°.
4. b) The sum is 360°.
Conclusions
The sum of the exterior angles of any polygon is 360°.

3.6E Using Dynamic Geometry to Prove Geometric Theorems: Angles   p. 179

1., 2.   Answers may vary slightly.

m∠ABD = 39.4°
m∠DBC = 50.6°
m∠ABD + m∠DBC = 90.0°

m∠EGH = 62.8°
m∠HGF = 117.2°
m∠EGH + m∠HGF = 180.0°

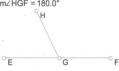

m∠IMK = 92.6°
m∠KMJ = 87.4°
m∠JML = 92.6°
m∠LMI = 87.4°

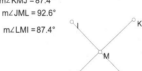

m∠NOP = 51.8°
m∠OPN = 59.1°
m∠PNO = 69.2°
m∠NOP + m∠OPN + m∠PNO = 180.0°

3.   CA - Two angles whose sum is 90°
     SA - Two angles whose sum is 180°
     OAT - Opposite angles formed by two intersecting lines are equal
     ASTT - The sum of the angles in a triangle is 180°
Practice
Answers may vary slightly.
1. a) $x = 70°$; CA
   b) $y = 155°$; SA; $x = 25°$, $z = 155°$; OAT
   c) $x = 55°$; ASTT   d) $x = 135°$; SA
   e) $5x = 125°$, $3x + 50° = 125°$; OAT; $y = 155°$; SA
   f) $x = 30°$, $x + 30° = 60°$, $x + 60° = 90°$; ASTT

3.6F Using Dynamic Geometry to Prove Geometric Theorems: Parallel Lines p. 181

1., 2. Answers may vary slightly.

m∠AGH = 77.3°
m∠BGH = 102.7°
m∠DHG = 77.3°
m∠CHG = 102.7°

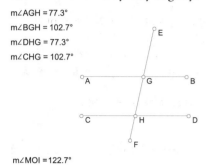

m∠MOI = 122.7°
m∠JOP = 122.7°
m∠IOP = 57.3°
m∠LPO = 57.3°
m∠LPN = 122.7°
m∠MOJ = 57.3°
m∠NPK = 57.3°
m∠KPO = 122.7°

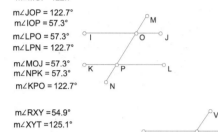

m∠RXY = 54.9°
m∠XYT = 125.1°
m∠SXY = 125.1°
m∠UYX = 54.9°
m∠RXY + m∠XYT = 180.0°
m∠SXY + m∠UYX = 180.0°

3. TPT Z - Angles that are between two parallel lines, and are on opposite sides of a transversal that intersects both parallel lines (alternate angles), are equal.

TPT F - Angles that are on the same side of a transversal that intersects two parallel lines, and are on the same side of the parallel lines (corresponding angles), are equal.

TPT C - Angles that are between two parallel lines, and are on the same side of a transversal that intersects both parallel lines (interior angles), add up to 180° (i.e., they are supplementary).

Practice
Answers may vary slightly.
1. a) $x = 20°$; TPT F; $y = 160°$; SA or OAT; $z = 160°$; TPT C
   b) $y = 95°$, $z = 85°$; SA; $x = 95°$; TPT F
   c) $x = 85°$; SA and TPT F or SA and TPT Z or OAT and TPT C
   d) $x = 135°$; TPT C
   e) $x = 30°$, $3x - 60° = 30°$; TPT Z; $y = 150°$; SA
   f) $5a - 30° = 20°$, $3a - 10° = 20°$; TPT F

3.6G Using Dynamic Geometry to Look at Quadrilaterals p. 183

1., 2. Answers may vary slightly.

m∠ABC = 116.1°
m∠BCD = 63.9°
m∠CDA = 68.0°
m∠DAB = 112.0°
m∠ABC + m∠BCD + m∠CDA + m∠DAB = 360.0°

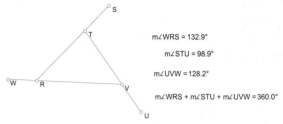

m∠WRS = 132.9°
m∠STU = 98.9°
m∠UVW = 128.2°
m∠WRS + m∠STU + m∠UVW = 360.0°

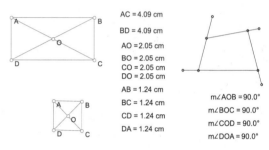

AC = 4.09 cm
BD = 4.09 cm
AO = 2.05 cm
BO = 2.05 cm
CO = 2.05 cm
DO = 2.05 cm
AB = 1.24 cm
BC = 1.24 cm
CD = 1.24 cm
DA = 1.24 cm

m∠AOB = 90.0°
m∠BOC = 90.0°
m∠COD = 90.0°
m∠DOA = 90.0°

3. Interior Angles of a Quadrilateral - The sum of the interior angles of a quadrilateral is 360°
Exterior Angles of a Triangle - The sum of the exterior angles of a triangle is 360°
Exterior Angles of a Quadrilateral - The sum of the exterior angles of a quadrilateral is 360°
Diagonals of a Rectangle - The length of the diagonals of a rectangle are equal, and they bisect each other
Diagonals of a Square - The diagonals of a square are perpendicular

Practice
a) 60° b) 36° c) 90° d) 4.5 cm

3.6H Circumcentre of a Triangle p. 185

Most answers will vary.
2. c) circumcentre
Conclusions/Observations
The circumcentre of a triangle is the point of intersection of the three perpendicular bisectors of the triangle; If one vertex of a triangle is a point on the circle whose centre is the circumcentre of a triangle, then the other two vertices will also be points on the circle, or, the circumcentre of a triangle is the centre of a circle, where all the vertices of the triangle lie on the circumference.

3.6I Triangle Centres and Their Properties

p. 187

1., 2.   Answers may vary slightly.

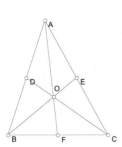

AO = 3.02 cm
OF = 1.51 cm
$\frac{AO}{OF}$ = 2.00
BO = 2.38 cm
OE = 1.19 cm
$\frac{BO}{OE}$ = 2.00
CO = 2.66 cm
OD = 1.33 cm
$\frac{CO}{OD}$ = 2.00

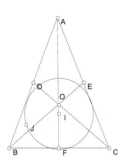

AO = 3.40 cm
OF = 1.70 cm
$\frac{AO}{OF}$ = 2.00
BO = 2.63 cm
OE = 1.31 cm
$\frac{BO}{OE}$ = 2.00
CO = 2.66 cm
OD = 1.33 cm
$\frac{CO}{OD}$ = 2.00

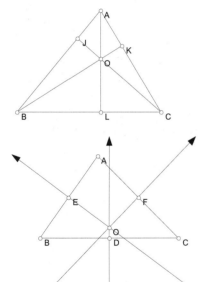

3.   Centroid - The point of intersection of the three medians in a triangle; the centroid is twice as far from the vertex as it is from the midpoint f the opposite side.

Incentre - The point of intersection of the three angle bisectors of a triangle; the incentre is the centre of the largest possible circle which can be inscribed in the triangle, which is adjacent to each side of the triangle

Orthocentre - The point of intersection of the three altitudes of a triangle: the orthocentre is inside acute triangles and it is outside obtuse triangles.

Circumcentre - The point of intersection of the three perpendicular bisectors of the triangle: the circumcentre is inside acute triangles and it is outside obtuse triangles.

3.7 Relations and *The Geometer's Sketchpad®*

3.7A Pi Demonstration (Again)

p. 189

All answers will vary.

6.

Diameter	Circumference	Ratio
7.01	22.02	3.14
4.51	14.18	3.14
6.35	19.95	3.14
6.67	20.95	3.14

Conclusion

The circumference of a circle is about 3.14 times the length of the diameter; $C = \pi d$.

3.7B The Pythagorean Theorem Using *The Geometer's Sketchpad®*

p. 190

All answers will vary.

6.

$(AB)^2 + (BC)^2$	$(AC)^2$	Observations
24.81	24.81	equal
29.73	29.73	equal
22.59	22.59	equal
12.56	12.56	equal

7.   In any right triangle, the square of the hypotenuse is equal to the sum of the squares of the other two sides; $a^2 + b^2 = c^2$

3.7C Equations of Lines and *The Geometer's Sketchpad®*

p. 191

All answers will vary.

5.   positive slope: $y = 0.6x + 4.6$
negative slope: $y = -0.4x + 1.4$
horizontal line: $y = -1$
vertical line: $x = -1$

3.7D Family of Lines: Activity

p. 192

2. $m = -2$; $b = 4$; $y = -2x + 4$
3. $y = -4x + 6$; the slope changes; the y-intercept stays the same.

Teacher's Resource Answers

Unit 3   Relationships in Geometry

A3.1E Area and Perimeter p. 128

Part A

1., 2., 3.   Answers may vary.

Part B

deck paint, area; aluminum, area; trim, perimeter; fence, perimeter; railing, perimeter; topsoil, area

Part C

1. a)   138 cm^2 b)   24 m^2
2. a)   9 m   b)   50 m
3. a)   390 m^2 b) $1161.62
4. a)   54.8 m   b) $900.56   c) $315.20
5. a) , b), c), d)   Answers may vary.

A 3.3B Circles p. 132

1.   100.48 cm   2.   38.5 m^2
3.   Answers may vary.
4. a) $183.88   b) $192.95   c) $433.35

A3.3C Area and Perimeter p. 134

1.   321.14 cm^2
2. a)   6.68 m   b) $22.50

A3.4B Pythagorean Theorem p. 135

1.   24.5 cm   2.   3.9 m

A3.5 B Paint and Walls p. 136

1. a)   Answers may vary.
    b)   36 m^2 c) $39.33

A3.5E Area and Volume p. 137

1. a)   2.3 m^3 b)   Yes   c)   13.92 m^2

A3.6F Angle Relations p. 140

1. a) $x = 140°, y = 40°$ b)   45°
    c) $x = 50°, \angle ABC = 130°$ d) $x = 62°$
    e) $x = 138°, y = 42°, m = 138°, q = 138°$
    f) $x = 40°, \angle ABC = 160°, \angle BCD = 160°$
2.   Answers may vary.

A3.6G Prove a Theorem pp. 141–142

4.   equal, parallel
5. a)   TQ ∥ SR, TS ∥ QR   b)   TQ = SR, TS = QR
6. a)   30° ∠LKM and ∠KMN are alternate angles formed by KL ∥ NM

b)   20°, ASTT
c)   20° ∠LMK and ∠MKN are alternate angles formed by KN ∥ LM

Unit 3 Assessment: Measure, Measure, Measure. pp. 143–147

1.   2.14 cm^2
2.   Prisms: 2, 6, 7, 8
3. a)   The volume of a pyramid is one third the volume of a prism.
    b)   Answers may vary.
4. a)   210 m^3 b)   38
5. a)   Answers may vary   b)   10.6 m^3 c)   .76 m
6. a)   33 m   b)   13 m
7. a), d)   Answers may vary.
    b)   85 100 m^2 c) $425 500
8. a)

Length (m)	Width (m)	Area (m)
1	11	11
2	10	20
3	9	27
4	8	32
5	7	35
6	6	36

b)
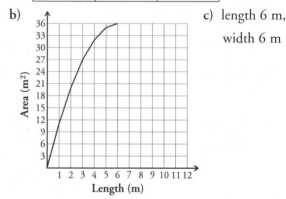

c) length 6 m, width 6 m

A3 Sketchpad Assessment pp148–149

Answers may vary
a)   ∠ABC = 90°; angle on a circle and subtended by a diameter
b)   ∠BCA = 42°; ASTT
c)   ∠BAD + ∠BCD = 180°

Learning Styles Inventory

Learn about yourself!
Answer each of the following questions about yourself by placing a
check mark (✔) beside the answer that you think best describes you.

1. If I have to learn how to do something, I learn best when I:

    (V) watch someone show me how.

    (A) hear someone tell me how.

    (K) try to do it myself.

2. When I read, I often find that I:

    (V) visualize what I am reading in my mind's eye.

    (A) read out loud or hear the words inside my head.

    (K) fidget and try to "feel" the content.

3. When asked to give directions, I:

    (V) see the actual places in my mind as I say them or prefer to draw them.

    (A) have no difficulty in giving them verbally.

    (K) have to point or move my body as I give them.

4. If I am unsure how to spell a word, I:

    (V) write it in order to determine if it looks right.

    (A) spell it out loud in order to determine if it sounds right.

    (K) write it in order to determine if it feels right.

5. When I write, I:

    (V) am concerned how neat and well-spaced my letters and words appear.

    (A) often say the letters and words to myself.

    (K) push hard on my pen or pencil and can feel the flow of the words or letters
    as I form them.

6. If I had to remember a list of items, I would remember it best if I:

    (V) wrote down the items.

    (A) said the items over and over to myself.

    (K) moved around and used my fingers to name each item.

7. I prefer teachers who:

    (V) use the board or overhead projector while they lecture.

    (A) talk with a lot of expression.

    (K) use hands-on activities.

8. When trying to concentrate, I have a difficult time when:

    (V) there is a lot of clutter or movement in the room.

    (A) there is a lot of noise in the room.

    (K) I have to sit still for any length of time.

9. When solving a problem, I

    (V) write or draw diagrams to see it.

    (A) talk myself through it.

    (K) use my entire body or move objects to help me think.

10. When given written instructions on how to build something, I:

    (V) read them silently and try to visualize how the parts will fit together.

    (A) read them out loud and talk to myself as I put the parts together.

    (K) try to put the parts together first and read later.

11. To keep occupied while waiting, I:

    (V) look around, stare, or read.

    (A) talk or listen to others.

    (K) walk around, manipulate things with my hands, or move/shake my feet as I sit.

12. If I had to describe something verbally to another person, I would:

(V) be brief because I do not like to talk at length.

(A) go into great detail because I like to talk.

(K) gesture and move around while talking.

13. If someone were verbally describing something to me, I would:

(V) try to visualize what the person was saying.

(A) enjoy listening, but want to interrupt and talk myself.

(K) become bored if the person's description were too long and detailed.

14. When trying to recall names, I remember:

(V) faces, but forget names.

(A) names, but forget faces.

(K) the situation that I met the person, rather than the person's name or face.

Scoring Instructions

Enter, in the table below, the total number of responses for each letter. The letter with the highest number of responses is probably your primary mode of learning. Because most people learn through a mixture of all three styles, read all the learning suggestions given and select those you feel will work best for you.

Visual	Auditory	Kinesthetic
V = _____	A = _____	K = _____

Name _____   Date _____

Learning to Study Through Critical Thinking by *Jonelle A. Beatrice*
(The following are some clues about what it means to be a certain style
of learner. Find your leaning style and read the clues and learning tips.)

Learning Styles—Clues and Learning Tips   Middlesex Community College

Clues

Visual Learners Usually:

- Need to see it to know it.
- Have strong sense of colour.
- Have artistic ability.
- Have difficulty with spoken directions.
- Over-react to sounds.
- Have trouble following lectures.
- Misinterpret words.

Auditory Learners Usually:

- Prefer to get information by listening—they need to hear it to know it.
- Have difficulty following written directions.
- Have difficulty with reading.
- Have problems with writing.
- Are unable to read body language and facial expressions.

Kinesthetic Learners Usually:

- Prefer hands-on learning.
- Can assemble parts without reading directions.
- Have difficulty sitting still.
- Learn better when physical activity is involved.
- Are very well coordinated and have athletic ability.

Learning Tips

Visual Learners Should:

- Use graphics to reinforce learning (films, slides, illustrations, diagrams, and doodles).
- Colour code to organize notes and possessions.
- Ask for written directions.
- Use flow charts and diagrams for notetaking.
- Visualize the spelling of words or facts to be memorized.

Auditory Learners Should:

- Use tapes for reading and for class and lecture notes.
- Learn by interviewing or by participating in discussions.
- Have test questions or directions read aloud or put on tape.

Kinesthetic Learners Should:

- Engage in experiential learning (making models, doing lab work, and role playing).
- Take frequent breaks in study periods.
- Trace letters and words to learn spelling and to remember facts.
- Use a computer to reinforce learning through sense of touch.
- Memorize or drill while walking or exercising.
- Express abilities through dance, drama, or gymnastics.

Adapted from the *Tutor Trainer's Manual*, Tyler Junior College, Tyler, TX.
Middlesex Community College
100 Training Hill Road, Middletown, CT 06457

Finding Relationships: Investigation

Experiment: _____

1. Make a **hypothesis** about the relationship.

   ☞

   ☞

   ☞

   ☞

   ☞

2. With your group, go to the assigned station and investigate your hypothesis by **gathering** and **organizing** the data.

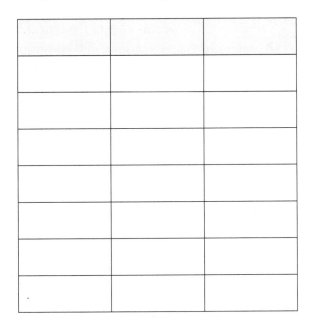
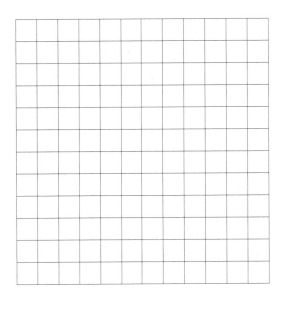

3. Create a **scatter plot** of your relationship (individually).
4. Draw the **line (or curve) of best fit** (individually).
5. Discuss the results with your group and record the relationship. Refer to your hypothesis and your graph.

Experiment Marking Checklist

1. **Communication**

    A: Hypothesis/Conclusion stated in full

    • linear, non-linear

    • positive/negative/none

    • statement of relationship of variables

    • origin in or out

    • data discrete or continuous

    B: Data entered correctly and accurately

    C: Graphs

    • titled

    • properly labelled

2. **Knowledge**

    A: Scales mathematically correct

    B: Data plotted accurately

    C: Appropriate lines or curves of best fit created

Total

Height of Object vs. Length of Shadow

Procedure

Caution: Do not move the lamp during this experiment.

Step 1   Choose one of the items available and stand it on the indicated line.

Step 2   Measure and record the height of the object and the length of its shadow in the chart provided.

Step 3   Repeat steps 1 and 2 for five more objects.

    a)   Make a hypothesis.

    b)   Complete a scatter plot.

    c)   Draw the line of best fit.

    d)   Describe the relationship.

Mass vs. Distance of Bag From Floor

Procedure

Step 1 Hang a plastic bag from an elastic band. Measure and record the distance from the bottom of the bag to the floor.

Step 2 Add one book to the bag. Measure and record the distance from the bottom of the bag to the floor.

Step 3 Repeat Step 2, adding one book at a time, until there are 8 books in the bag.

    a) Make a hypothesis.

    b) Complete a scatter plot.

    c) Draw the line of best fit.

    d) Describe the relationship.

Mass vs. Number of Books

Procedure

Step 1 Measure and record the mass of one copy of the book provided.

Step 2 Repeat step 1, adding one book at a time, until there are 8 books on the weighing scales.

Step 3 Record all data on the chart provided.

    a) Make a hypothesis.

    b) Complete a scatter plot.

    c) Draw the line of best fit.

    d) Describe the relationship.

Length of Pendulum vs. Time

Procedure

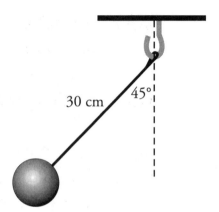

Step 1 Attach the large weight to the end of the pendulum string.

Step 2 Set the length of the pendulum string at 30 cm.

Step 3 Release the pendulum from a 45° angle and start the timer.

Step 4 Measure and record the length of time for five (5) complete swings.

Step 5 Repeat steps 3 and 4 for pendulum lengths of 40 cm, 50 cm, 60 cm, and so on.

a) Make a hypothesis.

b) Complete a scatter plot.

c) Draw the line of best fit.

d) Describe the relationship.

Mass of Pendulum vs. Time

Procedure

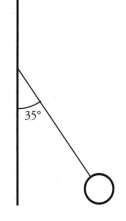

Step 1 Attach one weight (washer) to the end of the pendulum string.

Step 2 Set an appropriate length for the pendulum string.

Step 3 Release the pendulum from a 35° angle and start the timer.

Step 4 Measure and record the length of time for five complete swings.

Step 5 Repeat steps 3 and 4 after increasing the mass at the end of the pendulum by one washer each time.

    a) Make a hypothesis.

    b) Complete a scatter plot.

    c) Draw the line of best fit.

    d) Describe the relationship.

Height vs. Diameter

Procedure

Step 1 Choose a cylinder. Measure and record the height and diameter in the chart provided.

Step 2 Repeat step 1 for five more cylinders.

    a) Make a hypothesis.

    b) Complete a scatter plot.

    c) Draw the line of best fit.

    d) Describe the relationship.

Pieces of Chocolate Bar Remaining vs. Number of Bites

Procedure

Every time you take a bite of the chocolate bar, you eat half $\left(\frac{1}{2}\right)$ of what remains.

Record the number of pieces of the bar that **remain** after 0 bites, 1 bite, 2 bites, ..., up to 6 bites.

Use the second page of this master to help you visualize the problem.

1. **a)** Make a hypothesis.

    b) Complete a scatter plot.

    c) Draw the line of best fit.

    d) Describe the relationship.

2. Discuss how many bites are needed to finish the chocolate bar.

Chocolate Bar Piece	Chocolate Bar Piece	Chocolate Bar Piece	Chocolate Bar Piece
Chocolate Bar Piece	Chocolate Bar Piece	Chocolate Bar Piece	Chocolate Bar Piece
Chocolate Bar Piece	Chocolate Bar Piece	Chocolate Bar Piece	Chocolate Bar Piece
Chocolate Bar Piece	Chocolate Bar Piece	Chocolate Bar Piece	Chocolate Bar Piece
Chocolate Bar Piece	Chocolate Bar Piece	Chocolate Bar Piece	Chocolate Bar Piece
Chocolate Bar Piece	Chocolate Bar Piece	Chocolate Bar Piece	Chocolate Bar Piece
Chocolate Bar Piece	Chocolate Bar Piece	Chocolate Bar Piece	Chocolate Bar Piece
Chocolate Bar Piece	Chocolate Bar Piece	Chocolate Bar Piece	Chocolate Bar Piece

Area vs. Length of the Side of a Square

Procedure

Step 1   On grid paper, draw a square of side length 1 cm.

Step 2   Measure and record the area of the square.

Step 3   Repeat Steps 1 and 2 for squares with sides measuring 2 cm, 3 cm, 4 cm, and so on.

a)   Make a hypothesis.

b)   Complete a scatter plot.

c)   Draw the line of best fit.

d)   Describe the relationship.

Volume vs. Length of the Side of a Cube

Procedure

Step 1 Select a cube with a side of length one unit.

Step 2 Measure and record the volume of the cube.

Step 3 Repeat steps 1 and 2 for cubes with sides measuring 2 units, 3 units, 4 units, and so on. (It may be necessary to build them.)

  a) Make a hypothesis.

  b) Complete a scatter plot.

  c) Draw the line of best fit.

  d) Describe the relationship.

Comparison Shopping

Plan A Equation

Plan B Equation

Plan C Equation

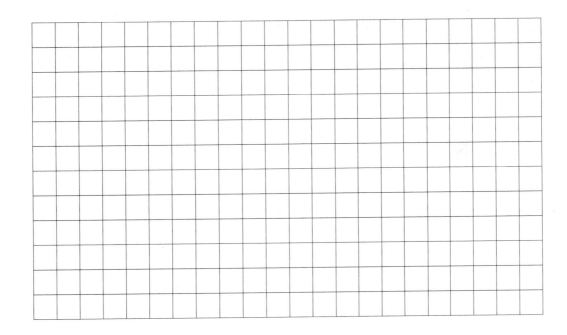

Conclusion

You would choose plan A if | You would choose plan B if | You would choose plan C if

Pythagorean Theorem Puzzle

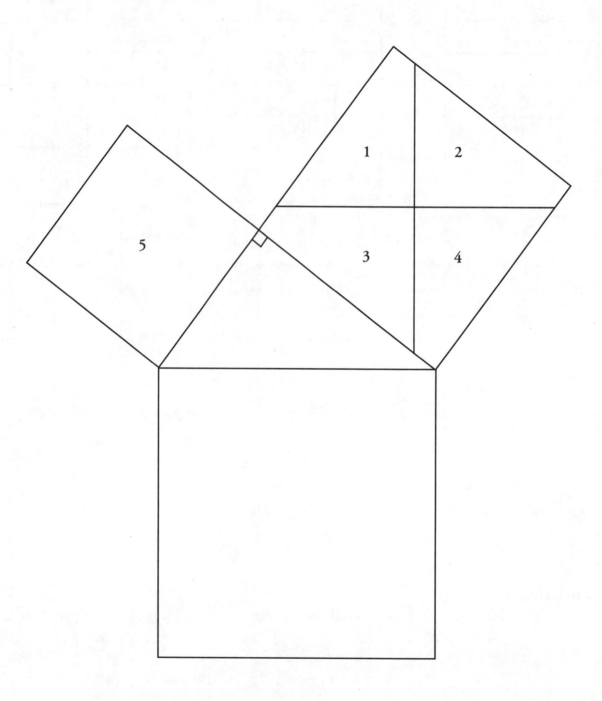

Three-Dimensional Geometry Solids:
Surface Area

Name of Solid	Net of Solid Made Up of ____ □s + ____ ◯s + ____ △s	Surface Area of Solid

Credits

Illustration Credits

© 2002 www.arttoday.com: 16, 20, 79; **Adobe Systems Incorporated:** 79, 143, 145; **Corel Corporation:** 14, 21, 24, 26, 68–69, 71, 85–88, 93–95, 143

Photo Credits

P. 15, Texas Instruments Incorporated

Text Credits

P. 60 and p. 114, Harvey Silver, Leadership@work, Toronto: LifeWorks Books, © 2001; p. 159, Adapted from the Tutor Trainer's Manual, Tyler Junior College, Tyler, TX, Middlesex Community College, 100 Training Hill Road, Middletown, CT 06457